Steve Parish

Amazing Facts about Australian
Reptiles

Text and Photography: Stephen Swanson

AMAZING FACTS — AUSTRALIAN REPTILES

Contents

INTRODUCTION

AUSTRALIA'S amazing reptiles   **4**

LIFESTYLE & diet   **6**

ALL-TERRAIN ANIMALS — adapted for land & sea   **8**

PREDATORS & prey   **10**

FINDING a mate   **11**

REPTILIAN reproduction   **12**

CROCODILIA

CROCODILES — at the water's edge   **16**

TESTUDINES

MARINE TURTLES — extraordinary navigators   **20**

FRESHWATER TURTLES — built like tanks   **24**

SQUAMATA (SAURIA)

LIZARDS — all shapes & sizes **30**

GECKOES — noisy night-hunters **32**

LEGLESS LIZARDS — snake look-alikes **36**

DRAGONS — alert & swift **38**

MONITORS — the largest lizards **44**

SKINKS — worldwide distribution **48**

SQUAMATA (SERPENTES)

SNAKES — slender magnificence **54**

BLIND SNAKES — earthworm impersonators **56**

PYTHONS — masses of muscle **58**

FILE SNAKES — unlikely to win a beauty contest **62**

COLUBRID SNAKES — harmless land snakes **64**

WATER SNAKES — aquatic ambushers **66**

FRONT-FANGED LAND SNAKES — venomous & abundant **68**

MARINE SNAKES — sea snakes & sea kraits **74**

REPTILES & PEOPLE — loved or loathed? **76**

GLOSSARY **79**

INDEX **80**

JOHN CANN

IAN MORRIS

IAN MORRIS

STEVE PARISH

STEVE PARISH

STEVE PARISH

Australia's
amazing reptiles

Reptiles have a long and illustrious history. During the "Age of Reptiles", for almost 200 million years spanning the Triassic and Cretaceous periods, reptiles were the dominant vertebrate animals on Earth. Included within their ranks were the spectacular dinosaurs, flying pterosaurs and sea-going mosasaurs.

FIRST LAND DWELLERS

Reptiles were the first vertebrates (animals with a backbone) to fully colonise the land surface. Their immediate ancestors, the amphibians, must periodically return to the water, or at least to a damp place to prevent dehydration and to lay their fragile eggs. The development of the amniotic egg (a fluid-filled sac for the embryo, encased in a durable shell), enabled reptiles to lay their eggs in dry places on land. Effectively, the fluid-filled amnion is a secure, aquatic environment in miniature for the developing reptile embryo. Unlike an amphibian, an adult reptile's scaly skin helps protect it from drying out away from the water.

Above, top to bottom: Muttaburrasaurus lived during the "Age of Reptiles"; Dinosaurs were egg-laying reptiles. Right: Gippsland Water Dragon.

the FACTS!

FOSSIL RECORDS indicate that reptiles evolved from amphibians in the Permian period, some 300 million years ago.

THE OLDEST KNOWN REPTILE is a lizard-like creature named *Pseudobradypus*. Its 315 million-year-old footprints were found preserved in mud in New Brunswick, Canada, in 2007.

WHEN REPTILES LEFT their amphibian ancestors behind in the swamp, there were no birds or mammals on land. These evolved from reptiles at a much later date.

WHAT IS A REPTILE?

Reptiles are four-legged vertebrates known as tetrapods, a group that includes all vertebrate animals except fish. Even snakes, which do not have any legs, are considered to be tetrapods, because they evolved from four-legged ancestors.

The class Reptilia can be seen largely as a grouping of convenience, best described as comprising the higher vertebrate animals (amniotes) excluding the birds and mammals.

There are four orders of living reptiles:

Order **CROCODILIA** — crocodiles and their kin the alligators, caimans and gharials.
Order **TESTUDINES** — turtles and tortoises.
Order **RHYNCHOCEPHALIA** — the lizard-like tuataras of New Zealand.
Order **SQUAMATA** — lizards, snakes and amphisbaenians (legless burrowing relatives of snakes and lizards that are found mostly in Africa, South America and the Middle East).

Australia's reptiles include crocodiles, freshwater turtles, marine turtles, lizards and snakes. Some 95% of living species fall within the order squamata, making lizards and snakes clearly the most successful modern reptiles. The turtles, crocodiles and tuataras are remnants of a once flourishing reptile fauna of a bygone era.

TURTLE, CROCODILE, LIZARD OR SNAKE?

Encased in their bony shell (or exoskeleton), Australia's turtles cannot be mistaken for anything but what they are. Crocodiles, however, are lizard-like in general body shape and a small one could be mistaken for a lizard. In northern Australia, people sometimes think a swimming Mertens' Water Monitor (*Varanus mertensi*) is a crocodile.

The classification of lizards and snakes together in the same order, distinct from other reptiles, suggests a closer relationship than might at first seem obvious. Crocodiles appear superficially more lizard-like than a limbless and elongate snake. However, lizards and snakes are indeed closely related, with snakes branching from lizards at a comparatively recent point along the path of reptile evolution. It is widely accepted that the snake's primitive ancestors were degenerate-limbed burrowing lizards, perhaps similar to burrowing members of some modern lizard families.

At first glance, the difference between lizards and snakes is apparent. Typically, a snake differs from a lizard because it is longer, lacks limbs and ears, has a sinuous, forked tongue and has a fixed, transparent scale covering the eye. But each of these features is also found among lizards! Conversely, some snakes have traces of hindlimb structures as a reminder of their lizard origins. So there are some lizards without limbs and some snakes with rudimentary limbs. Scientists use the structure of the jaws to separate snakes from lizards. The joints of a snake's jaw bones are attached with highly elasticised ligaments, enabling them to stretch apart to swallow prey much larger than the snake's head. Most lizards have limited jaw movements that work in much the same way as our own. All lizards, including legless species, have both pectoral (shoulder) and pelvic (hip) girdles, (the internal bone structures that support the limbs), but no snakes have pectoral girdles and only a few primitive families have traces of pelvic girdles.

Below: Amniotic eggs allowed reptiles such as the ancient Kalisuchus *(bottom) and the more modern Estuarine Crocodile (*Crocodylus porosus*, below) to colonise the land.*

the FACTS!

THE "AGE OF REPTILES" ended about 65 million years ago with a rather abrupt mass extinction of most kinds of dinosaur. Why the dinosaurs and many other reptiles disappeared so suddenly remains a mystery.

PTEROSAURS (top right) may look like birds, but most palaeontologists consider them to be flying reptiles. Others speculate that pterosaurs and some other extinct dinosaurs were "warm-blooded" and question whether they belong within the class Reptilia at all!

SOME SCIENTISTS believe that crocodiles are more closely related to birds than to other members of the class Reptilia.

AN INCREASINGLY ACCEPTED view is that birds evolved from dinosaurs. According to a classification system based on ancestry (cladistics), birds belong in the Class Reptilia.

Lifestyle
& diet

STEVE PARISH

Above: A Lace Monitor (*Varanus varius*) effortlessly scales a tree.

the FACTS!

AUSTRALIA HAS about 880 reptiles and new species are being discovered each year.

TWO GENERA of small skinks, the striped skinks (*Ctenotus*) and sliders (*Lerista*), contain an astonishing 175 species between them.

IN THE SUBURBS OF SYDNEY, the Fence Skink (*Cryptoblepharus pulcher*) is more common on paling fences than it is in adjacent bushland.

THE LAKE EYRE DRAGON (*Ctenophorus maculosus*, below) inhabits perhaps the most inhospitable environment that Australia has to offer, on the fringes of the vast salt lakes of arid South Australia. It shelters under buckled sheets of the salt lake's crust.

IAN MORRIS

IAN MORRIS

Top: The spiny skin of a Thorny Devil (*Moloch horridus*) soaks up water from wet sand and channels it to the lizard's mouth. *Above:* Ring-tailed Dragons (*Ctenophorus caudicinctus*) are also designed for dry conditions.

ARID-ADAPTED COLONISERS

Australia is home to a diverse range of reptiles, which occupy all corners of the continent. Because they rely on heat from the sun to warm their bodies to a functioning temperature, they are most abundant in the tropical north and decline in the south, where there is less sunshine. Only three snake species, confined to one family, occur in Tasmania, but 43 species from six families exist in the Top End of the Northern Territory. Having said that, Australia's reptiles do make use of a wide range of environments. In the south-east, the Highlands Copperhead (*Austrelaps ramsayi*) lives above the snow line in alpine meadows. The aquatic Arafura File Snake (*Acrochordus arafurae*) lives in rivers and swamps in tropical northern Australia. The Reef Shallows Sea Snake (*Aipysurus duboisii*) and the Hawksbill Turtle (*Eretmochelys imbricata*) swim in the warm waters of the Great Barrier Reef. White-bellied Mangrove Snakes (*Fordonia leucobalia*) and Rusty Monitors (*Varanus semiremex*) make their home in mangrove swamps. The Narrow-banded Sand Swimmer (*Eremiascincus fasciolatus*) burrows among dunes in the Simpson Desert, and in north-eastern Queensland, Prickly Forest Skinks (*Gnypetoscincus queenslandiae*) burrow under logs on the rainforest floor. Even in the suburbs of Sydney, Eastern Long-necked Turtles (*Chelodina longicollis*) seem to be thriving in polluted ponds and drains.

LEFT: KEN STEPNELL; BELOW: STEVE PARISH

Left: Green Turtles (*Chelonia mydas*) nest along the Queensland coastline.

LEFT: MICHAEL CERMAK

IAN MORRIS

VORACIOUS PREDATORS

Most reptiles are carnivores that eat other animals, although some are omnivores that consume both plant and animal food. A few are herbivores, feeding only on plants. Snakes and crocodiles are exclusively carnivorous.

CROCODILES PREY ON any animal they can seize and hold on to, and an adult Estuarine Crocodile (*Crocodylus porosus*) will take large animals such as cattle, horses and humans. Hatchlings survive on insects and frogs.

MOST LIZARDS ARE CARNIVOROUS and insects are their preferred diet. However some, such as Cunningham's Skink (*Egernia cunninghami*), feed mainly on plants but will eat insects and worms if the opportunity arises. Termites are abundant throughout much of Australia, particularly in arid and tropical regions, and are an important food source for lizards. The extraordinary diversity of small lizards in arid Australia is largely due to the availability of termites for them to eat. Large monitor lizards include carrion in their diet and are often observed on the side of the road feeding on roadkill.

FRESHWATER TURTLES can be either carnivorous or omnivorous. Carnivorous long-necked turtles ambush fish with an explosive strike of their long, powerful neck, but short-necked turtles are unable to catch swimming fish and mostly eat plants. Some marine turtles are herbivorous, browsing on algae and sea-grass, while others feed on sea jellies, sponges or shellfish.

ALL AUSTRALIAN SNAKES (with the exception of the crab-eating White-bellied Mangrove Snake (*Fordonia leucobalia*) and the blind snakes in the genus *Ramphotyphlops*) eat vertebrate animals (or their eggs), including other reptiles, frogs, fish, mammals and birds. The prey may be overpowered by constriction, an injection of venom, or a combination of both, before being swallowed whole. The unique White-bellied Mangrove Snake swallows small crabs whole, but pulls the limbs off larger crabs and swallows them piece by piece. It is the only snake known to dismember its prey. Blind snakes feed exclusively on the eggs, larvae and pupae of ants and termites.

Below: An unlucky amphibian makes a meal for a Freckled Monitor (Varanus tristis orientalis).

IAN MORRIS

Above, left to right: Estuarine Crocodiles eat other reptiles and fish as well as mammals and birds; A Pilbara Olive Python (*Liasis olivaceus barroni*) takes on the difficult task of attempting to devour a wallaby.

the FACTS!

LARGE ESTUARINE CROCODILES use their tails to trap fish against the riverbank in shallow water. The fish are then seized as they attempt to escape to deeper water past the crocodile's jaws.

SMALL LIZARDS are the preferred diet of many snakes. The Northern Death Adder (*Acanthophis praelongus*, below) attracts lizards by wriggling the grub-like tip of its tail in front of its jaws.

LARGE MONITOR LIZARDS like the Lace Monitor (*Varanus varius*) and the Yellow-spotted Monitor (*Varanus panoptes*) frequent picnic areas and camping grounds searching for meat scraps left over from the barbecue.

All-terrain animals
— adapted for land & sea

STEVE PARISH

the FACTS!

REPTILES INHABIT all of the Earth's continents except Antarctica, with most species found in warm tropical regions.

THERE ARE more than 7 000 reptile species worldwide.

REPTILES' LIMBS project sideways from the body, giving them a "sprawling stance" and a "scuttling" motion. Mammals and birds have an upright stance, with their limbs extending beneath the body, directly down from the hips.

MAMMALS ARE now considered to be the Earth's dominant vertebrate animals, but reptiles are much more diverse, far exceeding mammals in number of species.

BIRDS AND MAMMALS remain more or less uniform in size once they reach adulthood, but reptiles continue to grow throughout their life, which explains records of reptiles much larger than their average adult size.

A number of special features — such as hard, protective scales, super-efficient waste processing systems and the ability to lay eggs that do not need to hatch in water — enabled reptiles to colonise both the land and the oceans. Combined, these physiological differences separate reptiles from other vertebrates.

SCALY SKIN-SHEDDERS

Unlike the feathers of birds, the hair (or fur) of mammals or the damp, naked skin of amphibians, reptiles are distinguished by skin that is protected by a covering of dry scales or hard, bony plates known as scutes. Snakes and lizards periodically shed the outer layer of their skin; how often they shed depends on their growth rate, age and health. When ready to shed, a snake's scales, including the transparent scale over the eye, become clouded, impairing the snake's vision. It begins to remove the skin by rubbing its lips against a rough surface and peeling it back from its head. The loose skin is snagged in a crevice or on a sharp rock and the snake emerges, inverting the skin in one long piece. Because of its more complex body form, a lizard's skin is usually discarded in pieces. Large monitors often have traces of previous sheddings in shreds and patches, giving them a somewhat untidy appearance. Turtles also cast off the outer layer of their shields (scutes) from the shell, particularly when young, and crocodiles moult the outer layer of their large scales individually.

OTHER ADAPTATIONS

Most reptiles (apart from crocodiles) have a three-chambered heart which is more primitive and, in some respects, less efficient than the four-chambered hearts of crocodiles, birds and mammals. However, what they lack in heart, reptiles make up for in water efficiency. A reptile's excretory system uses minimal water to flush waste from the body. Reptiles also differ from most mammals (apart from the Platypus and echidnas) in having a cloaca — a single opening at the base of the tail for excretory and reproductive processes. With their reduced requirement for water, along with their scaly skin which helps to reduce moisture loss, reptiles are able to live in very dry regions.

Below: Basking Freshwater Crocodiles (*Crocodylus johnstoni*).

Above: The Brisbane Short-necked Turtle (*Emydura macquarii signata*) is common in the waterways of south-eastern Queensland.

Top right: Estuarine Crocodiles are formidable predators.

Right: Stimson's Pythons (*Antaresia stimsoni*) are widespread in arid Australia but classified as Vulnerable in New South Wales.

EXTRA LONG LUNGS

Reptiles breathe through their lungs, although some sea snakes also receive some of their oxygen from the water through the skin. Freshwater turtles supplement their oxygen intake by drawing water into complex, gill-like sacs, within the cloaca. Because of their elongate bodies, snakes have room for only one lung. The left lung is either greatly reduced in size, or absent. In some aquatic snakes, the lung extends almost the entire length of the body.

NOT SO COLD-BLOODED

Reptiles are often referred to as "cold-blooded", setting them apart from the "warm-blooded" birds and mammals, but this term is not very accurate. There is nothing cold about a reptile's blood! A better word to describe a reptile is "ectothermic". Unlike birds and mammals, which are "endothermic" and generate heat from within their bodies, ectothermic animals regulate their body temperature externally, using heat from the sun's rays or from a heated ground surface, rock, or log. Ectothermic animals are more energy efficient than endothermic birds and mammals, which must constantly find food to fuel their internal heating.

To maintain a functional body temperature, a reptile shuttles backwards and forwards between a warm basking site and a shaded site. Turtles float in warm water on the surface to increase their body temperature, while crocodiles bask on exposed river banks and slip back into the water to cool off. To fine tune its thermoregulation, a basking dragon lizard maintains an upright stance, balanced on its tail and hindlimbs, and a skink folds its limbs up against its flanks to decrease body contact with a hot surface and reduce its body temperature. Numerous reptile species are able to survive so well in tropical climates and deserts because they are ectothermic. Reptiles in cold climates hibernate during the winter months.

the FACTS!

SOMETIMES an Eastern Blue Tongue (*Tiliqua scincoides scincoides*) will eat its shed skin. It may do this to recover nutrients from the skin, or perhaps to remove signs of its presence from possible predators.

OCCASIONALLY, BASKING groups of lizards such as Burton's Snake Lizards (*Lialis burtonis*) and Fence Skinks (*Cryptoblepharus pulcher*) are encountered. Such groups could be mating groups, or perhaps the lizards have recently emerged from a common winter shelter site and are warming their bodies in the sun before dispersing. It is not always apparent why a number of individuals choose to occupy the same hibernation site, when it is not obviously superior to other shelter sites nearby.

SMALL GROUPS of female Red-bellied Black Snakes (*Pseudechis porphyriacus*) may share a common shelter and basking site in summer. Whether they are taking advantage of an optimum location, or simply see safety in numbers, is not understood.

Predators
& prey

Most reptiles are near the bottom of the food chain, so they continually have to avoid predators. Threats can come from unlikely directions — even other reptiles are a threat — so a reptile's first line of defence is usually to remain unseen. If a reptile realises that its cover has been blown, it has to choose between fighting or fleeing.

ELUDING PREDATORS

Other reptiles and birds are not the only animals preying on reptiles; fish are also a threat and some, such as the Goldspotted Rockcod (*Epinephelus coioides*), will quickly make a meal of a White-bellied Mangrove Snake if it strays into deep water. Small lizards are also sometimes ambushed by insects and arthropods, such as mantids (*Mantodea* spp.) and Red-backed Spiders (*Latrodectus hasselti*). Camouflage is a common method of escaping detection, and species such as the Southern Forest Dragon can easily be overlooked.

The Lace Monitor (*Varanus varius*) prefers to flee, and usually escapes by scaling a tall tree. Many other lizards, like the Central Netted Dragon (*Ctenophorus nuchalis*) rarely stray far from their burrow and quickly disappear into it when approached. When a reptile's avenue of escape is blocked, it is time for pretence. A cornered Frilled Lizard (*Chlamydosaurus kingii*) stands on its hindlimbs, extends its frill and opens its mouth to face an aggressor. It uses every trick at its disposal to look larger and more fierce than it is, but at the first opportunity, turns and runs for the nearest tree.

JEAN-PAUL FERRERO/AUSCAPE

Above: A Lace Monitor battles a pair of hungry Dingoes.

A LAST RESORT — VENOMOUS TACTICS

As a last resort, some reptiles will bite — and in the case of the dangerously venomous King Brown Snake (*Pseudechis australis*), its bark is not worse than its bite! Australian reptiles like the King Brown Snake have evolved venom and a venom delivery system, primarily for securing their prey and helping them to digest their meals. However, they will sometimes also bite to defend themselves and some snakes can, of course, kill humans. Australia's dangerously venomous snakes are confined to the family Elapidae (front-fanged land snakes and marine snakes). Research has shown that some colubrid snakes and even lizards, which were previously regarded as non-venomous, in fact possess a mild venom, but their bite is still considered harmless to humans.

---

the FACTS!

BOTH THE Southern Forest Dragon (*Hypsilurus spinipes,* above) and the Southern Leaf-tailed Gecko (*Saltuarius swaini*) are found in the rainforest. Their mottled pattern and colour resembles the lichen-covered tree trunks on which they rest.

MITCHELL'S WATER MONITORS (*Varanus mitchelli*) drop into the water from overhanging tree branches and hide under litter on the bottom of the river.

WITH ITS DARK HEAD PATTERN and distinctive defensive posture, an Eastern Hooded Scaly-foot (*Pygopus schraderi*) appears to mimic a juvenile Western Brown Snake (*Pseudonaja nuchalis*). Under threat, it raises its forebody high off the ground and flicks its tongue in a snake-like manner.

IT WAS ONCE BELIEVED that only two lizards in the world, the Gila Monster (*Heloderma suspectum*) and the Beaded Lizard (*Heloderma horridum*), both of North America, were venomous. However research has found that some Australian lizards, including the Lace Monitor and the Central Bearded Dragon (*Pogona vitticeps,* below), also have venom glands.

THE VENOM of Australian lizards is mild and they lack an efficient means of delivering it. None of Australia's venomous lizards pose a threat to humans.

STEVE PARISH

Finding a mate

Above: Common Death Adders
(*Acanthophis antarcticus*)

Reptiles differ further from most mammals and amphibians in their mode of reproduction. Most reptiles lay eggs that are fertilised inside the female, whereas those of amphibians are fertilised externally, and young pass through an aquatic, gill-breathing stage. However, before they can even think of laying eggs, reptiles first need to find a mate.

GETTING TOGETHER

Most reptiles lead a solitary existence until the breeding season, when males actively seek out females. At this time, reptiles are often observed in pairs and occasionally in larger groups. Such groups, called aggregations, are either the result of a number of males seeking to mate with a single female, or multiple reptiles choosing the same shelter site for hibernation. Some sites contain large numbers of individuals (sometimes of more than one species) and are occupied year after year.

Some skinks, like the rock-dwelling Spiny-tailed Skink (*Egernia stokesii*), form stable, social groups made up of small numbers of differently sized individuals. These are considered "family" groups comprising a male and a female and their offspring of previous seasons. There is a lot of interaction between the members of such groups — they are not simply occupying a suitable shelter site together. Adult Cunningham's Skinks (*Egernia cunninghami*) have also been observed foraging in the company of newborn young, at some distance from their permanent shelter site.

In North America, snake "dens" that might contain thousands of snakes of various species are well documented. While such huge aggregations are unrecorded in Australia, groups of about 30 individuals of species including Small-eyed Snakes (*Cryptophis nigrescens*), South-eastern Blind Snakes (*Ramphotyphlops nigrescens*) and Eastern Brown Snakes (*Pseudonaja textilis*) are on record.

Small groups of Common Tree Snakes (*Dendrelaphis punctulata*) and Brown Tree Snakes (*Boiga irregularis*) shelter together in windblown sandstone caves in the Sydney region of New South Wales.

There are also sightings of huge swarms of marine snakes in the open sea, although the large numbers of Yellow-lipped Sea Kraits (*Laticauda colubrina*) which occur about exposed shipwrecks and small islets, are most probably just taking advantage of an ideal habitat.

Below: The Delicate Skink (*Lampropholis delicata*) is common in eastern suburban gardens.

Reptilian
reproduction

Above: The parthenogenetic Mourning Gecko. *Right:* Male (rear) and female Tawny Dragons (*Ctenophorus decresii*).

the FACTS!

THE STRIKING MALE Red-barred Dragon (*Ctenophorus vadnappa*) is one of Australia's most colourful lizards. During its territorial display, it lifts its tail in a high, vertical coil while slowly raising and lowering its body.

A MALE Open Litter Rainbow Skink (*Carlia pectoralis*) develops orange stripes on its flanks during the breeding season to increase its visibility. It further advertises its presence by lifting and waving its tail.

ALL RECORDED Flowerpot Snakes (*Ramphotyphlops braminus*) are female and it is assumed that it is a parthenogenetic species.

MALE FRILLED LIZARDS (*Chlamydosaurus kingii*, below) vigorously defend their territory from encroachment by another male. An old male often bears scars and a torn frill from such encounters.

MALE OR FEMALE?

It is usually difficult to tell males and females of most Australian reptiles apart. Only some lizards show an obvious variation in colour or form between the sexes (known as sexual dimorphism). Rainbow Skinks (*Carlia* spp.), are small, drab leaf-litter inhabitants, but in the breeding season, males of most species develop bold colours — presumably to enhance their visibility to ward off rival males. In Australia, sexual dimorphism is most noticeable among dragons. Apart from their more vibrant colouring, most male dragon lizards are larger, more robust and have more prominent spiny adornment than females.

MALE COMBAT

During the breeding season, male lizards and snakes of some species engage in fights that amount to largely ritualised combat. Some biting may occur, but serious injuries are not sustained very often. An encounter between rival male snakes includes lively pursuit, vigorous entwining of bodies and face to face confrontation with forebodies raised high. Some lizards, especially large monitors, rear onto their hindlimbs and tail and grapple with their opponent in a violent embrace. The unique social behaviour of dragons, which includes jerking head movements and circular waving of the forelimbs, intensifies during the mating season. If a dragon's visual signals fail to warn off a rival, a brief skirmish might occur. Adult male crocodiles are also fiercely territorial and will challenge or kill other males that venture into their territory.

Despite these masculine displays, some reptiles have found a way to do away with males entirely for reproductive purposes. The Mourning Gecko (*Lepidodactylus lugubris*, top left) produces viable eggs without input from a male, a process known as parthenogenesis. A parthenogenetic population consists entirely of females and all of the offspring are clones that are genetically identical to their mother.

Right: Male Yellow-spotted Monitors (*Varanus panoptes*) in combat.

IAN MORRIS

Above: Female Asian House Geckoes (*Hemidactylus frenatus*) lay two eggs per clutch.

STEVE PARISH

MATING & EGG-LAYING

In Australia's temperate regions, reptiles adhere to a predictable breeding timetable. Mating takes place in spring, the eggs are laid in early summer and the young hatch, or are born, in late summer. However, in tropical climates, where it is warm all year round, there is much variation. Some reptiles breed in the dry season (winter) and some in the wet season (summer); others appear to breed all year round.

All crocodiles and turtles, as well as most snakes and lizards, reproduce by laying eggs. An egg-laying (oviparous) turtle, snake or lizard, invests a lot of time and energy finding a suitable location and excavating a nest, but once the laying is complete, the eggs are left to the whims of nature. In Australia, only crocodiles and pythons care for their eggs after they are laid. Hatchling turtles, lizards and snakes are self reliant from the moment they tear themselves free of their eggshell. Some lizards and snakes are live-bearing (viviparous) and mostly dwell in cooler regions, where this reproductive method offers distinct advantages. A mobile lizard or snake carrying developing embryos has more control over their temperature by moving about in the environment, while eggs, once laid, are largely at the mercy of the elements and are vulnerable to predation.

the FACTS!

THE EGGS OF MOST REPTILES are encased in a flexible, leathery skin. Some, like those of crocodiles and some geckoes, are more rigid (calcareous), something like a bird's egg. When ready to hatch, the offspring break open the shell from the inside using a special "egg tooth" (a projection on the snout) that falls off soon after they hatch.

PUTTING ALL YOUR EGGS IN ONE BASKET

Females of some lizards or snakes may choose to deposit their eggs in a communal nesting site — even when it appears that there are many equally suitable but unused nesting sites nearby. Scientists who study reptiles do not fully understand why some reptiles choose to nest communally, but the behaviour of marine turtles gives us an idea of just how important some nest sites are to particular reptiles. Loggerhead Turtles (*Caretta caretta*) may swim thousands of kilometres across the Pacific Ocean, passing hundreds of sandy beaches along the way, to lay their eggs on one very special beach — the same beach on which they hatched.

Female marine turtles return to the beach of their birth to lay their eggs in a shallow sandy nest.

IAN MORRIS

Above: A hatching crocodile struggles to break free from its eggshell.

the FACTS!

RECENTLY HATCHED crocodiles form a "crèche" and stay in close proximity to one another for about five weeks among aquatic vegetation in shallow water. During this period the mother is usually close by to provide some protection from predators.

FEMALE CROCODILES sometimes assist their hatching young to break free of the eggshell and may carry them to the water in their mouths.

SNAKES' EGGS (below) are tough and leathery, so the baby snakes grow a modified projection called an "egg tooth" on the snout, which is used to pierce the shell. Baby birds also have an egg tooth, but the evolution of this feature is uncertain. In 2004, a 121-million-year-old fossilised egg and embryo of a bird-like dinosaur were discovered in China's north-east. The embryo has no egg tooth, which could mean that this feature is a relatively modern adaptation. Dinosaurs probably tore their way out of their shells using their claws.

MOST REPTILES never get to see their parents and vacate the nest independently soon after they hatch from the egg.

TO NEST OR NOT TO NEST

The Estuarine Crocodile (*Crocodylus porosus*) constructs a large mound nest consisting of composting vegetation and stands guard over the eggs until they hatch. Freshwater Crocodiles (*Crocodylus johnstoni*) lay their eggs in a hole scooped in a riverside sandbank. A female Freshwater Crocodile remains in the vicinity of the incubating eggs and opens the nest when the young are ready to hatch. But unlike crocodiles, few other reptiles bother to construct a nest for their eggs. Most snakes simply choose a suitable secluded site, beneath leaf litter, in a tree hollow, or under bark and rocks, to deposit their eggs. Some pythons make a nest of sorts by creating a depression among dense vegetation. Once their eggs are laid, the python usually remains coiled about them to help with their incubation and deter predators. Most lizards, like snakes, simply lay their eggs in a humid site beneath cover, or they may dig a burrow into the soil and deposit their eggs in a chamber at its end. Some lizards lay their eggs in the vacated burrow of another animal. With the exception of crocodiles, which stay near their young to offer protection, most reptile hatchlings are on their own once they break free of the eggshell. Some skinks and snakes produce living young which are ready to fend for themselves from birth.

ABSENT MOTHERS & CARING CROCS

Maternal care is rare among reptiles, but the obvious exception is the complex nesting behaviour of crocodiles. A female crocodile is a doting parent. The level of care she provides for her eggs and hatchlings is unparalleled in the reptile world and emphasises the crocodile's evolutionary relationship to birds.

The only other Australian reptiles to care for their eggs are pythons. They coil around them to keep them warm by "shivering" and to protect them from predators.

Right: Pythons such as the Green Tree Python (*Morelia viridis*) coil around their eggs to keep them warm.

14

STEVE PARISH

Left: Pig-nosed Turtles (*Carettochelys insculpta*) are a freshwater species whose sex is determined by temperature.

the FACTS!

WARMER EGGS at the top of the Pig-nosed Turtle's (left) nest produce females and cooler eggs below produce males. Some nests produce all females, or conversely, all males.

LIZARDS like the Southern Water Skink could be very vulnerable to climate change. It is estimated that a 4°C overall increase in the temperature of their habitat would produce only male offspring, soon making them extinct.

IN GENETICALLY sex determined reptiles, some females have XX chromosomes and males XY (as in humans), while in others males are ZZ and females ZW (as for birds).

IN 2007, scientists at the University of Canberra discovered that heat can make male Central Bearded Dragons (*Pogona vitticeps*, below) change sex in the shell and hatch as females — proving that temperature can override this species' genetic sex. When eggs were incubated at 34–37°C, most embryos that initially had ZZ (genetically male) sex chromosomes hatched as ZW (genetically female). This could mean the Central Bearded Dragon represents an evolutionary link between the two methods of sexual determination.

HOT OR COLD HATCHLINGS

The sex of most vertebrate animals' offspring is decided genetically at the time of fertilisation. But for some, including many reptiles, the sex of their young is determined by environmental factors following fertilisation — particularly by the incubation temperature of the eggs.

"Temperature Dependent Sex Determination" (or TDSD for short) is common among crocodiles and turtles and also in some dragon lizards like the Frilled Lizard (*Chlamydosaurus kingii*) and the Jacky Lizard (*Amphibolurus muricatus,* bottom left). Producing either males or females comes down to just a few degrees difference and the activation temperatures vary between the species. However it is not always a matter of warmer means one sex and cooler the other.

The eggs of the Estuarine Crocodile produce males in a mid-range temperature, with temperatures either side producing female offspring.

MATERNAL BASKING

Recent research has shown that some live-bearing skinks in southern Australia vary the sex ratio of their offspring by increasing or decreasing their basking activity while pregnant. By warming up, a pregnant female Ocellated Skink (*Niveoscincus ocellatus*) produces more female offspring. But a Southern Water Skink (*Eulamprus tympanum*) doing the same, produces more males. Whether the skinks choose to manipulate the sex of their offspring by varying their basking times, is a matter for debate.

Below: Jacky Lizard (*Amphibolurus muricatus*)

Below: Central Bearded Dragon (*Pogona vitticeps*)

Above: Estuarine Crocodiles are ferocious carnivores.

Crocodiles
— at the water's edge

Order: Crocodilia
Family: Crocodylidae

Crocodiles are ancient animals and have kept the same basic body plan for at least 100 million years. A modern crocodile is much the same as one that basked at the feet of dinosaurs. Life as a predator on the water's edge has been good to crocodiles.

NORTHERN AUSTRALIA is home to two species of crocodile: the widespread Estuarine Crocodile (*Crocodylus porosus*), which ranges from northern Australia to southern Asia, and the smaller Freshwater Crocodile (*Crocodylus johnstoni*), which lives only in Australia.

the FACTS!

THERE ARE 22 SPECIES of crocodile (including gharials, caimans and alligators) in the world and two of these inhabit northern Australia.

THE WORLD'S LARGEST REPTILE, the Estuarine Crocodile (top) is fully grown at 5 m, but occasionally reaches a length of 7 m and weighs as much as a tonne.

THERE ARE UNCONFIRMED historical reports of Estuarine Crocodiles shot during the last century measuring 8 m and even 10 m, but the largest on record is around 7 m.

THE ESTUARINE CROCODILE cannot live indefinitely in saltwater, but has been known to undertake sea voyages of over 1000 km.

ARMOURED, AMPHIBIOUS PREDATORS

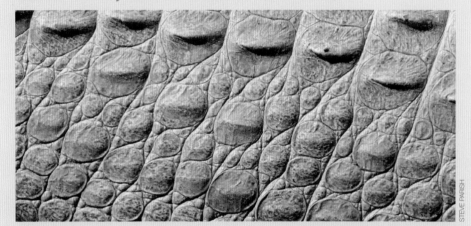

Crocodiles are superbly adapted, amphibious predators. Their body form is lizard-like, although larger, and their skin is covered in non-overlapping scales which are embedded with bony plates at their back and sides, providing a formidable armour. Their nostrils, eyes and ears are located on top of the head, allowing them to remain virtually submerged while breathing and use their keen senses of smell, sight and hearing to detect prey or danger. As well as conventional eyelids, crocodiles have a transparent third eyelid, called a nictitating membrane, which is drawn across the eye when the reptile goes under water. A large valve at the back of the throat seals off the gullet when a crocodile opens its mouth underwater, so its body doesn't fill with water. Crocodiles swim by sweeping their tails from side to side, holding their limbs firmly against the sides of the body.

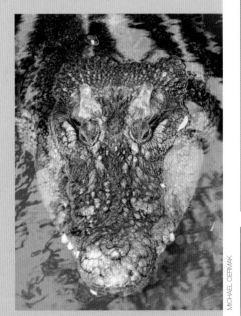

Above: A crocodile's teeth, visible at the side of the closed jaw, give it a permanently menacing appearance.

Right: Freshwater Crocodiles, unlike their larger kin, Estuarine Crocodiles (above), pose no threat to humans.

Conservation Watch
Continued protection of crocodiles in the wild and a carefully managed crocodile farming industry should ensure the survival of both Freshwater and Estuarine Crocodiles in Australia.

Above: Estuarine Crocodiles seize animals like this Antilopine Wallaroo (*Macropus antilopinus*) at the water's edge.

LARGEST, MOST DANGEROUS CROCODILE

At 7 m in length and weighing up to a tonne, a fully grown Estuarine Crocodile is the world's largest living reptile and a rival for the mythical sea monster. Apart from sharks, it is Australia's only predator of humans and inspires fear and fascination in the general population. It is also the world's most dangerous crocodile, an opportunistic feeder and ferocious predator. If you enter the water near a large Estuarine Crocodile, it is very likely you will be attacked and eaten. On average, two people are attacked by Estuarine Crocodiles every year in Australia, and about one in four of these attacks is fatal. Most people living in tropical Australia are well aware of how dangerous Estuarine Crocodiles are and their caution near waterways keeps the number of attacks relatively low. Not surprisingly, most attacks occur in the Northern Territory, which has the highest Estuarine Crocodile population.

the FACTS!

CROCODILES have five toes on the front feet but only four toes on each rear foot.

ESTUARINE CROCODILES, not alligators, bask on the banks of the Alligator River in the Northern Territory, which was given the name in error by early explorers. Alligators actually only occur in North America and China.

ACROSS NORTHERN AUSTRALIA, Estuarine Crocodiles are farmed for their skin, which produces a valuable leather, and also for their meat. In the Northern Territory, crocodile burgers are popular with tourists.

CROCODILES SWALLOW small stones (gastroliths) and these are held in the gizzard to help grind up food during digestion. The pebbles also act as ballast, helping a crocodile to keep stable in the water.

EFFICIENT PREDATORS

Crocodiles are active both during the day and at night. During the cooler months they are often observed basking in the sun at the water's edge. They eat a wide range of animals in relation to their size. Small crocodiles feed on insects, frogs, shrimp and fish, progressing to turtles, water snakes, birds, bats and small mammals. A large Estuarine Crocodile is even capable of overpowering a horse!

TERRITORIAL BEASTS

Male crocodiles are highly territorial. A large male controls a billabong or section of river, including its population of resident females and vigorously defends it from other male crocodiles. Fighting between large male crocodiles can result in death or serious injury to one of the combatants.

Below: Estuarine Crocodiles float like logs on the water's surface, leaving just their eyes and nostrils visible.

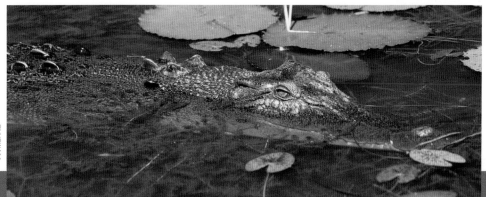

STEVE PARISH

RON & VALERIE TAYLOR

Top and above: Male "Freshies" grow to 3 m and females to 2 m.

STEVE PARISH

Above: A fully grown male "Saltie" measures 5–7 m and a female 3–4 m.

MOSTLY HARMLESS — "FRESHIES"

Freshwater Crocodiles, commonly known as "freshies" are fully grown at 3 m and as a rule do not attack people. Isolated records of bites from Freshwater Crocodiles are probably due to the crocodile mistaking the moving limbs of a swimmer for food, or are in response to the crocodile feeling threatened by an intrusion into its territory. When it feels threatened on land, a Freshwater Crocodile "gallops" to the safety of the water with both front limbs and both hindlimbs moving in unison. In a short burst, it can reach a speed of almost 20 km/h, which is about as fast as any crocodile can go.

In the wet season, Freshwater Crocodiles are common in freshwater rivers, swamps, billabongs and seasonal creeks. In the dry season, they return to permanent waterholes or take refuge in burrows beneath overhanging dry creek banks. From July to September in the dry season, females lay about twelve eggs in a hole scooped in a sand bank. When they begin to hatch about 80 days later, the juveniles make a "chirping" call, which is a signal to the female to come and dig them from the sand. Once in the water, the young form a group and the mother usually remains close by to provide some protection from predators. Large fish, birds, freshwater turtles and other crocodiles all prey on hatchlings, and many nests are destroyed by feral pigs and monitor lizards even before the young hatch.

FEROCIOUS DEFENDERS — "SALTIES"

The Estuarine Crocodile, sometimes called the Saltwater Crocodile or the "saltie", is not restricted to saltwater as its name suggests. It lives in a range of aquatic environments, from freshwater swamps and billabongs, to tidal rivers, estuaries and coastal waters. During the wet season, when much of the land is flooded, it swims to isolated waterholes and may remain there after the flood waters recede. This means it may be safe to swim in a waterhole in Australia's north one year, but not the next.

Estuarine Crocodiles characteristically ambush and seize large animals at the water's edge. The crocodile rotates its body (the so-called death roll) causing the animal to loose its footing and then drags it into the water to drown. Animals too large to swallow whole are torn into bite-sized pieces by violent shaking and twisting. Fruit bats often roost in large numbers in trees bordering tropical rivers and Estuarine Crocodiles are known to lurk near such colonies, snapping up any bat unfortunate enough to fall into the water (right).

MICHAEL CERMAK

Conservation Watch

"Sustainable use" programs reward land owners for preservation of wild crocodiles and their habitats.

BETWEEN NOVEMBER AND MARCH in the wet season, female Estuarine Crocodiles construct mound-like nests of plant matter and mud, usually within 10 m of the river's edge. The elevated nest helps prevent egg loss if water levels rise. In freshwater swamps, nests may be built on a floating mat of vegetation. About 50 eggs are laid and the female stays nearby to guard the nest from predators. The eggs hatch after about 90 days, when the mother returns to the nest to release the hatchlings, which signal their readiness with a chirping call. Amazingly, the mother may help the tiny hatchlings to the water by carrying them gently in her mouth. The young usually stay in a group, or crèche, for about five weeks and the female is often close by to ward off predators during this period.

Above, left and right: Crocodile farms harvest "crocs" sustainably for leather and meat. One farm, in Darwin, is attempting to map the Estuarine Crocodile's DNA in order to improve the leather.

A SECURE FUTURE

Some crocodile populations throughout the world are endangered: threatened by habitat destruction and over-exploited for their skins. In Australia, crocodiles were hunted extensively for their skins and their numbers suffered such a decline that by the late 1960s it was feared they might become extinct. This led to their protection across northern Australia by the early 1970s. Protection of wild populations, and the introduction of a carefully managed crocodile farming industry, has led to a remarkable recovery of crocodile numbers. The future of both the Freshwater Crocodile and the Estuarine Crocodile in Australia now appears to be secure. However, some populations of Estuarine Crocodiles in other parts of its range outside of Australia remain seriously at risk of local extinction.

SUSTAINABLE USE

In the Northern Territory, sustainable use programs for the Estuarine Crocodile have been operating for a number of years. Landowners, often Aborigines, are paid a royalty for crocodile eggs collected from their land, which provides an ongoing incentive for them to preserve both the crocodiles and their habitat. The eggs are hatched and the hatchlings sold on to commercial crocodile farms for raising and skin production. Surveys of wild populations have indicated that the harvesting of eggs has no impact on population numbers.

the FACTS!

FOR EVERY 100 EGGS laid, only one crocodile survives to reach maturity.

CROCODILES HAVE been found to have excellent "homing" and navigational instincts. In one study conducted by the University of Queensland, crocodiles that had been airlifted up to 126 km away from their territory returned within weeks. One even covered 411 km in just 20 days to reach its old hunting grounds!

"CROCODILE TEARS" flow from a crocodile's eyes when it is out of the water, and folklore has it that they are showing sympathy for their victims. In fact, the "tears" are simply to lubricate the nictitating membrane, or third eyelid.

CROCODILES ARE the most vocal reptiles. Juveniles chirp to be released from their nest, and adults might roar, bellow or hiss.

A CROCODILE'S CLOACA (vent at the base of the tail) is aligned lengthwise, unlike that of snakes and lizards, which is aligned sideways.

A CROCODILE'S TEETH (below) are designed to lock onto its prey once it is seized and are of little use for cutting or chewing. Worn and broken teeth are continually replenished and a crocodile might replace as many as 2 000 teeth during its lifetime.

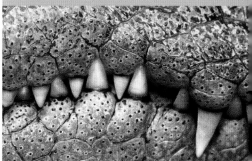

Above: Turtles cruise the ocean before returning to nest on the specific Great Barrier Reef (or other tropical Australian) beach where they hatched.

Marine turtles
— extraordinary navigators

Order: Testudines
Families: Cheloniidae & Dermochelyidae

There are seven species of marine turtle in the world and six of them swim in Australian waters and nest on our beaches. Most occur in tropical waters, with occasional stragglers wandering further south.

the FACTS!

THE FLATBACK TURTLE has the smallest distribution of all marine turtles and is considered Vulnerable in Australia.

SOME SCIENTISTS BELIEVE that the world's largest turtle, the Leatherback Turtle, will be extinct within the next few decades if current global fishing practices continue.

UNTIL THE MID-1900s, the Hawksbill Turtle was heavily exploited for its attractive shell (tortoiseshell), which was used to make combs or filigree jewellery.

A ROBOTIC TURTLE named Madeleine, which was developed in 2006 based on the body shape of a Pacific Ridley Turtle, is helping scientists study underwater locomotion. Madeleine's polyurethane flippers are operated by a motor that is controlled by a computer onboard the robot. Researchers hope to construct better subaquatic "flippered" research vessels from the studies, but it could also tell us more about how far, and fast, turtles can swim.

ALL AUSTRALIAN MARINE TURTLES, except the Flatback Turtle (*Natator depressus*), range well outside our continental waters and can be considered international species. This makes it difficult to put conservation measures in place for their protection. In Australia, the most commonly seen species are the Flatback Turtle, the Green Turtle (*Chelonia mydas*), and the Loggerhead Turtle (*Caretta caretta*), with the Pacific Ridley Turtle (*Lepidochelys olivacea*), Hawksbill Turtle (*Eretmochelys imbricata*) and Leatherback Turtle (*Dermochelys coriacea*) less often observed. All are vulnerable to extinction. With the exception of the Leatherback Turtle, which wanders the open oceans (making it "pelagic"), most marine turtles inhabit shallow coastal waters. Most are also migratory and may travel thousands of kilometres between their feeding grounds and nesting beaches.

POWERFUL SWIMMERS

In contrast to the clawed feet of most freshwater turtles (except for the Pig-nosed Turtle), marine turtles have paddle-shaped limbs, making them powerful swimmers. Employing their large forelimbs in the manner that a bird uses its wings, they propel themselves through the water at speeds up to 35 km/h. They are also much larger than their freshwater

Above, top to bottom: Hawksbill Turtle; Loggerhead Turtle; Marine turtles use their front flippers for propulsion and their back flippers to steer and brake.

relatives and their carapace (top shell) is more streamlined. Another difference is that a marine turtle is unable to retract its head and flippers into its shell the way freshwater turtles do.

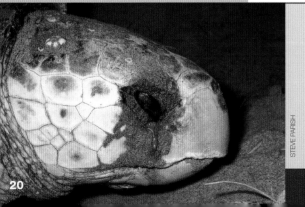

SALTY TEARS

Marine turtles do not need to drink freshwater; they get what they need from their diet or from metabolising seawater. Excess salt in a marine turtle's body is released as tears from glands in the eyes. This is seen in nesting females, with the briny discharge also helping to keep sand out of her eyes while she digs her nest.

Left: While it is a struggle for female marine turtles to clamber out of the water to lay eggs, the tears are not from exhaustion — they excrete excess salt and protect her eyes from the sand.

MORRIS

STEVE PARISH

TURTLE TUCKER

Marine turtles may be either carnivorous, omnivorous or, as in the case of adult Green Turtles, herbivorous. Strangely, juvenile Green Turtles are carnivorous, but as they grow, their diet changes and they feed almost exclusively on algae and seagrass. The Loggerhead Turtle is a large-headed carnivorous turtle that dines on a wide variety of invertebrates, including shellfish, crabs, shrimps, sea jellies and sea urchins. The Hawksbill Turtle gets its name from its hooked, parrot-like upper jaw, which it uses to snatch up sponges and pick off marine algae. Pacific Ridley Turtles prefer crabs and shellfish. The Flatback Turtle is confined to the waters of northern Australia and southern New Guinea, where it feeds mainly on soft corals and sea jellies.

ENORMOUS & UNIQUE

The Leatherback Turtle is the sole member of the family Dermochelyidae and the word "unique" has never been more appropriately used than in describing this enormous reptile. It is a pelagic (open water) turtle, swimming across vast expanses of ocean searching for the sea jellies on which it feeds. The Leatherback Turtle is also the world's most widespread reptile, inhabiting all tropical and temperate seas and straying as far south as New Zealand and as far north as Iceland. Its huge size — up to 2.5 m in carapace (top shell) length and weighing 900 kg — almost rivals the size of the Estuarine Crocodile. Unlike the horny scutes that cover the shells of other marine turtles, the shell of the Leatherback Turtle has a thick, leathery covering and is long and streamlined, with prominent ridges running along the carapace and plastron (lower shell). In Australia, Leatherback Turtles occur in coastal waters around much of the continent, but most migrate to New Guinea and Indonesia to breed. A few scattered nests are recorded around Bundaberg in Queensland and in Arnhem Land in the Northern Territory.

the FACTS!

MARINE TURTLES have existed for more than 150 million years.

IN THE POLLUTED OCEANS, Leatherback Turtles mistake floating plastic bags for sea jellies. If swallowed, the plastic bags form blockages in their stomachs and intestines, and are a significant cause of untimely deaths.

THE LEATHERBACK TURTLE inhabits the open ocean and dives to depths in excess of 1 100 m seeking sea jellies, including the stinging Bluebottle, which it consumes in large numbers.

A GREEN TURTLE'S CARAPACE can be over a metre wide and can weigh up to 150 kg.

FOR MANY YEARS, marine turtle researchers have attached tags or, more recently, satellite transmitters to turtles in an effort to better understand their migratory patterns.

LEATHERBACK TURTLES tolerate colder water better than other marine turtles. A combination of large size and excellent body insulation, enables them to maintain their temperature up to 18°C higher than that of the surrounding water.

REMORAS, OR SUCKER FISH, will hitch a ride by attaching themselves to a marine turtle's shell.

RON & VALERIE TAYLOR

Left: The huge Leatherback Turtle has very long front flippers and a ridged, "leather-like" shell from which it takes its common name.

Above, left to right: Turtles gather to breed; Return to the sea after egg-laying; Sometimes more than one male attempts to mate with a single female.

the FACTS!

FEMALE FLATBACK TURTLES nest only in Australia and are at least 20 years old before they are first ready to lay eggs. Loggerhead Turtles may not reach sexual maturity until they are 35 years old!

FEMALE MARINE TURTLES can retain sperm from one season's mating to fertilise eggs in the following season.

Below: Hatchlings that make it to the water swim solo until, decades later, they are ready to reproduce.

A LIFE AT SEA

Marine turtles spend their lives at sea, with only the females leaving the water to lay their eggs on the land. Males and females migrate over long distances, returning to the beach where they hatched to mate and lay their eggs. They remain in the waters off the nesting beach for the duration of the breeding season and the females come ashore several times to lay clutches of eggs — it may be two to five years before she returns to nest again.

Some breeding groups contain thousands of individual turtles, with males vying for females to mate with, and females vying for a position on the beach to lay their eggs. At high tide, under the cover of darkness, a female hauls herself out of the water and laboriously climbs up the beach to a point above the high tide mark. She uses all four limbs to scrape out a pit for her body to rest in, then with the hindlimbs alone, excavates the flask-shaped egg chamber. About 50–100, and occasionally as many as 200, round, white eggs are deposited into the nest, with the turtle carefully directing them into position with her rear flippers. Once the laying is completed, she backfills and compacts the nest site and, now exhausted, returns to the water. A female may spend two or more hours out of the water during the nesting process. The sex of the incubating turtles is determined by the nest temperature: cooler temperatures produce more males and warmer temperatures more females.

A SCRAMBLE TO SURVIVE

Marine turtles produce large numbers of eggs because only a very small percentage of hatchlings survive to reach maturity. Monitor lizards and other predators sometimes dig up turtle nests to devour the eggs before they even develop. Eggs hatch about 7–10 weeks after they are laid. Once the eggs hatch, the 5 cm long hatchlings might take a few days just to dig upwards through the sand, from perhaps a metre or more of depth, to just below the beach surface. They then usually wait until nightfall to emerge. Having never before seen the ocean, they hurriedly and instinctively seek the water and proceed to clamber and race en masse past a gauntlet of predators such as gulls and crabs. With death possible at every turn, there is no time to take in their surroundings. Those that do survive the perilous journey to the water face sharks and other predators in the sea. Once in the water, the hatchlings swim frantically for one or two days until they reach the comparative safety of deeper water.

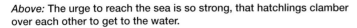

Conservation Watch

Many thousands of marine turtles die annually in nets or on the hooks of long-line fishers. Until this issue is addressed globally, the prospects for the long-term survival of many species appears bleak.

Above: The urge to reach the sea is so strong, that hatchlings clamber over each other to get to the water.

BACK TO THE FUTURE

Little is known of the hatchlings' biology or movements for the first year or so of life. They are probably carried along by currents on the ocean's surface, and feed on small marine invertebrates among floating mats of algae and debris. They may even swim thousands of kilometres — sometimes across entire oceans — while they feed and grow.

One thing is certain — decades later, once they reach sexual maturity, they will return to the very beach on which they were born to mate and lay eggs. Each turtle is living proof of the suitability of this particular beach as a site for their own eggs. A female turtle's logic appears to be, "if you're on to a good thing, stick to it"— and stick to it marine turtles have done, for more than 100 million years!

STEVE PARISH

Above: Hatchlings instinctively emerge from their shells and dig their way out of the nest at night. Getting to the water by moonlight is fraught with danger, and many are picked off by predators.

the FACTS!

WHEN HATCHLING TURTLES emerge at night from beach nests that are near a town or settlement, they often become disoriented and head towards the lights. This leads them away from the water and into dangerous terrain, where they wander about until they succumb to dehydration, are run over on roads or are eaten by predators.

A LOGGERHEAD TURTLE that was tracked from its feeding grounds off the Mexican coast, across the Pacific Ocean to a nesting beach in Japan, had travelled a total of 15 000 km!

MASTER MARINERS

The long-distance migration of marine turtles — in particular their ability to navigate across thousands of kilometres of seemingly featureless ocean with pinpoint accuracy — is one of the marvels of the natural world. However, it is their return to the precise beach of their own birth to lay their eggs that is truly astonishing. How they do it and why they do it, is an enduring mystery. Recent research has shown that marine turtles possess an extra sense that enables them to detect the Earth's magnetic field, which could explain their exceptional navigation skills. The position of the sun and stars, as well as ocean currents, may also play a role.

Freshwater turtles
— built like tanks

Order: Testudines
Families: Cheluidae & Carettochelyidae

A freshwater turtle's hard shell — and the fact that it can withdraw its body parts into it — is its main defence. Furthermore, it is a system that has worked for many millions of years!

FRESHWATER TURTLES are aquatic reptiles, inhabiting swamps, ponds, lakes, creeks and rivers. They leave the water to lay eggs on land. If the water they live in dries up, they may be forced to move to another watercourse. None are able to feed, or exist permanently out of the water.

A freshwater turtle's shell consists of a carapace (top shell) that is fused to the turtle's backbone and ribs, and a plastron (lower shell). These are joined at the sides by bony "bridges". With the exception of the Pig-nosed Turtle (*Carettochelys insculpta*), the shell is covered with symmetrically arranged plates (known as scutes) and these are shed off individually as the turtle grows. Turtles have no teeth; instead the jaws have horny cutting edges.

the FACTS!

TURTLE OR TORTOISE? In the past, Australia's freshwater turtles were popularly called "tortoises", but the more appropriate name of "turtle" is now being used. In most parts of the world, the word tortoise is reserved for members of the terrestrial (land-dwelling) family Testudinidae. There are no terrestrial tortoises in Australia.

INCLUDING SUBSPECIES, there are 36 kinds of freshwater turtles in Australia and new species are regularly being described.

THE EASTERN LONG-NECKED Turtle (below) was the first Australian freshwater turtle known to science. It was collected by Captain James Cook's naturalist, Joseph Banks, in 1770, probably near Sydney, New South Wales.

Above: Eastern Long-necked Turtles, like all reptiles, bask in the sun to regulate their temperature.

PULL YOUR HEAD IN

Side-necked turtles in the family Cheluidae occur only in Australasia and South America, providing further evidence that the two continents were once joined in the supercontinent of Gondwana. Marsupials (pouched mammals) are also found only in Australasia and South America. Side-necked turtles withdraw their heads beneath their carapaces by folding their necks to the side, and are known as pleurodires. Most of the world's turtles pull their head directly back into the shell, and so are cryptodires. In Australia, only the Pig-Nosed Turtle is a cryptodire.

Above: An Eastern Long-necked Turtle with head and limbs retracted.

STEVE PARISH

Conservation Watch

Humans threaten the survival of freshwater turtles indirectly, by interfering with or polluting the waterways that are essential to their existence.

Testudines

HIBERNATION & AESTIVATION

Some side-necked turtles leave the water to hibernate during winter or aestivate during summer. During these inactive periods, a turtle's metabolism slows down, almost to a stop. They barely breathe and stop eating, instead surviving on accumulated body fat. As winter arrives and the water temperature drops, turtles in some parts of the country enter hibernation. They can hibernate either on land or in the water. If they hibernate on land, they burrow into the soil, usually in leaf litter or under a fallen log, as protection from frost. Turtles hibernating under water can stay submerged for long periods, taking in oxygen through their cloacas.

Some turtles aestivate in summer, when the watercourse they are occupying dries up. The Western Swamp Turtle (*Pseudemydura umbrina*) lives in temporary swamps and must aestivate for about 5–8 months each summer. In the Northern Territory, Northern Long-necked Turtles (*Chelodina rugosa*) dig into mud at the bottom when the water level of their lagoon drops during the dry season. When the lagoon dries completely, they are left encased in mud beneath the ground and must wait for wet season rains to refill the lagoon. Aborigines like to eat Northern Long-necked Turtles and probe the dry lagoon bed with a sharp stick searching for the sleeping turtles. Steindachner's Long-necked Turtle (*Chelodina steindachneri*) inhabits dry parts of Western Australia and scientists know very little about its life history. In some areas, it appears in temporary creeks and ponds after heavy rain, apparently after aestivating for long periods underground.

JOHN CANN

Above: The Critically Endangered Western Swamp Turtle.

the FACTS!

AUSTRALIA'S SMALLEST turtle, the Western Swamp Turtle, is the only turtle known to dig its nesting chamber with its front limbs.

THE WESTERN SWAMP TURTLE is confined to a very small area near Perth, Western Australia. But it was once more widespread. A *Pseudemydura* species fossil some 15 million years old was found at Riversleigh in north-eastern Queensland.

Below: When threatened, as by this Great Cormorant, freshwater turtles simply withdraw their heads.

A STINKER

The Eastern Long-necked Turtle (*Chelodina longicollis*) is also known as the Common Long-necked Turtle. It moves about between watercourses more often than other turtles, probably to take advantage of the abundance of food provided by recently filled waterholes. It is the most common and familiar turtle of eastern Australia and motorists are often called upon to rescue it from busy highways. It is also called "stinker", and anyone who has ever picked one up off the road will readily agree with the suitability of this name. When distressed, it squirts a powerful and obnoxious smelling liquid from glands at the base of its legs, a strategy that deters most predators. In eastern Australia, it is the most commonly kept pet turtle and soon stops producing its strong odour once it becomes accustomed to being handled. Hatchling Eastern Long-necked Turtles have strongly contrasting orange and black colouring underneath their shell. This is a warning colour for would-be predators, and the warning is, "don't eat me, I'm not very tasty".

IAN MORRIS

JOHN CANN

Above and left: Northern Long-necked Turtles have speckled markings on the head.

STEVE PARISH

Above: Most freshwater turtles, such as this Eastern Long-necked Turtle must regularly come to the surface to breathe.

STEVE PARISH

the FACTS!

FROM THE MOMENT they break free of the eggshell, hatchling freshwater turtles face many predators and only a small percentage survive to adulthood.

PREDATORS OF FRESHWATER turtles include sea-eagles, which pluck them from the surface of the water, as well as crocodiles and water-rats.

FRESHWATER TURTLES regularly drown in traps and nets, or die after swallowing fish hooks.

MANY FRESHWATER TURTLES die when the water they are living in dries up during a drought, or is diverted for irrigation.

Below: Short-necked turtles regularly climb from the water onto logs to bask.

LEFT: IAN MORRIS; RIGHT: JOHN CANN

Conservation Watch

The Mary River Turtle occurs only in the Mary River of south-eastern Queensland. An increasing amount of development planned for this area makes the future of this already endangered turtle even more uncertain.

THE LONG & SHORT OF IT

Australian side-necked turtles are either short-necked or long-necked. Short-necked turtles are omnivorous, feeding mainly on algae and aquatic plants, as well as fruit, leaves and blossoms that fall into the water from plants at the water's edge. They also eat shrimp, shellfish and insects. While they cannot swim fast enough to catch live fish, they will eat dead fish, animals or birds when they have the chance. Short-necked turtles have five claws on each front leg.

Long-necked turtles are carnivorous. Fish are ambushed with a rapid strike of the long neck and sucked into the gaping mouth. Long-necked turtles also eat frogs, tadpoles, shrimp and insects in their diet, but do not eat plants. Long-necked turtles have four claws on each front leg.

"BUM BREATHING"

Side-necked turtles spend most of their time underwater and breathe by stealthily bringing the tip of their snout to the surface. Most can also take in some oxygen from the water through highly specialised pouches in the cloaca. Oxygen is also taken up through the skin or lining of the mouth and throat.

Some turtles are better at getting oxygen from the water than others. The Fitzroy River Turtle (*Rheodytes leukops,* below) of eastern Queensland, rarely needs to visit the surface to breathe. It has highly specialised cloacal sacs (chambers inside the vent at the base of the tail) and obtains much of its oxygen from the water by "breathing" through the cloacal opening, which has led to it being known as the "bum-breathing turtle". It pumps water in and out of its cloacal opening up to 60 times a minute!

The Mary River Turtle (*Elusor macrurus*) is also known to take in oxygen through its cloacal vent in the same way the Fitzroy River Turtle does.

Below: Fitzroy River Turtles extract oxygen from water taken into the cloaca.

KEEPING WARM

Side-necked turtles, particularly short-necked turtles, bask in the sun by climbing from the water onto the bank, a log or rock. They do this to raise their body temperature and help digestion. It also helps the turtle rid itself of parasites such as leeches. A turtle also raises its body temperature by floating in warm water at the surface.

Below: The freshwater Pig-nosed Turtle's huge flippers are more like those of marine turtles than those of other freshwater turtles.

STEVE PARISH

Below: The Victoria River Turtle grows to around 22 cm in length.

JOHN CANN

TELLING TURTLES APART

Because Australia is a dry continent, it is home to fewer freshwater turtles than most other regions of the world. Many turtles in other countries of the globe have bright colouration and striking patterns, but Australian turtles are often dull in comparison. Juveniles are usually more colourful than adults, but the colouring fades as the turtles mature.

It is difficult to tell male and female freshwater turtles apart. A mature female is usually larger and more deep-bodied than her mate. Her deeper shell provides the extra space needed to carry eggs. Male turtles usually have a larger tail than females.

Above: The courtship behaviour of side-necked turtles occurs underwater and is rarely observed.

STEVE PARISH

SUB-AQUATIC SEX

Some glimpses of the underwater courtship behaviour of side-necked turtles has shown the male bobbing his head, gently stroking the female's face with his claws and pushing against her body with his snout. Mating takes place underwater, with the male mounting and gripping the carapace (top shell) of the female from above, or occasionally in a belly to belly position.

NESTING

When ready to nest, a female freshwater turtle leaves the water and digs a pear-shaped nest with her hindlimbs, usually in sandy or loamy soil. She chooses a sunny position near the water's edge, above the high water mark. After carefully laying the eggs, she backfills the nest and returns to the water. Her work is now done and the eggs are on their own.

Despite the female's best efforts, the eggs are far from safe. Predators, such as foxes and monitor lizards sometimes dig up the nest and eat the eggs. If flooding causes the water level to rise above the nest, the developing embryos will drown while in the eggshell.

BOOF-HEAD!

The Victoria River Turtle (*Emydura victoriae*) lives in the Victoria and Daly Rivers of the Northern Territory. It has a broad, reddish or yellow stripe on either side of its face, so it is sometimes also known as the Northern Red-faced Turtle. However, because its head becomes very large with old age, it is more commonly called the Boof-headed Turtle. It is thought that the large head is an adaptation for crushing the shells of mussels, a favourite food item for this species.

the FACTS!

THE RECENTLY DESCRIBED Irwin's Snapping Turtle (*Elseya irwini*) was named in honour of the late "Crocodile Hunter" Steve Irwin, who first brought it to scientific attention.

UNIQUELY, SOME POPULATIONS of Northern Long-necked Turtles lay their eggs underwater — no other turtle in the world is known to do this! The eggs are laid in the mud, in shallow water at the edge of a drying lagoon. The eggs remain in limbo while still covered by water and only begin to develop when the nesting site dries up. The eggs of all other turtles would drown when covered by water.

Above: Cooper Creek Turtle

Above: Bumpy skin protrusions on the Western Swamp Turtle's neck are known as "tubercles".

the FACTS!

THE MARY RIVER TURTLE'S genus name, *Elusor* (elusive) refers to the question of its whereabouts for many years — until it was discovered in the Mary River, from which it takes its common name.

A MALE MARY RIVER TURTLE (above) has a very long, thick tail that can measure up to 70% of its shell length.

FRESHWATER TURTLES are remarkably long-lived. A pet turtle bought by a child might still be part of the family when its owner grows to adulthood. There are records of Eastern Long-necked Turtles living in captivity for more than 50 years!

ABORIGINES throughout Australia consider many freshwater turtle species good to eat.

THE PET SHOP TURTLE

With a shell length of 42 cm, the Mary River Turtle (*Elusor macrurus*) is Australia's largest short-necked turtle. Despite its size, it was only described by science in 1994, but researchers had known about it for many years from hatchlings that were commonly sold in pet shops as "penny tortoises". At the time, no one was able to discover where these mysterious "penny tortoises" lived in the wild. It occurs only in the Mary River of south-eastern Queensland and is considered an endangered species. The small Mary River system is under considerable pressure from surrounding farming activity and other planned developments in the area could have severe consequences for populations of this turtle in the wild.

COOPER CREEK TURTLE

The Cooper Creek Turtle (*Emydura macquarii emmotti*) is another side-necked turtle that was only described very recently. Like the Mary River Turtle, scientists have known about it for some years — it just took them a long time to decide how this species fits in with its near relatives. It is a large side-necked turtle, measuring up to 37 cm in shell length and weighing 7.25 kg. The Cooper Creek Turtle occurs only in the Cooper Creek drainage, a large river system comprising a string of isolated waterholes that begin in western Queensland and end at Lake Eyre in South Australia. The creek flows only after prolonged rain. The turtles' pale yellow-grey colouring matches the always-muddied waters of its habitat.

Below: Cooper Creek Turtles dwell in isolated waterholes of the Cooper Creek drainage, a waterway between western Queensland and South Australia that rarely flows.

Conservation Watch

The world's rarest turtle, the Western Swamp Turtle (*Pseudemydura umbrina*) is teetering on the brink of extinction, with perhaps only 100 turtles remaining in the wild.

JOHN CANN

RED-BELLIED TURTLE

The Red-bellied Turtle (*Emydura subglobosa*) is Australia's most colourful freshwater turtle, with bright yellow facial stripes and red colouring on the neck and underside of the shell. It is a common, widespread turtle in New Guinea, but in Australia it is recorded only in the Jardine River, the northernmost river of Cape York Peninsula, Queensland. As is the case with much of the Cape York fauna, there were species radiations to Australia from New Guinea when the two land-masses were joined at a time of lower sea levels.

Above: The Red-bellied Turtle is Australia's most colourful freshwater turtle species.

UNIQUE PIG-NOSED TURTLE

The Pig-nosed Turtle (*Carettochelys insculpta*) of northern Australia and southern New Guinea is the sole member of the *Carettochelyidae* family. Unlike all other Australian freshwater turtles, it withdraws its head directly into its shell instead of turning it to the side. It also has flipper-like limbs rather than strong claws, and webbed feet like those of the side-necked turtles. As its name suggests, its snout is soft and protruding, a bit like that of a pig. Originally known from the Fly River in Papua New Guinea, it was not until 1970 that this turtle was discovered in the Daly River, Northern Territory. Of course Aboriginal people knew of its existence all along; in Kakadu they called it *Warradjan*, and regularly hunted it for food. It inhabits freshwater rivers and billabongs during the dry season and swims well out into flooded plains during the wet season. Like marine turtles, the Pig-nosed Turtle is fully aquatic. It does not bask on land and leaves the water only to lay eggs. The eggs resemble ping-pong balls and are laid in a nest scooped in a sandy bank near the water. Like crocodiles, the sex of hatchling Pig-nosed Turtles is determined by the incubation temperature of the eggs inside the nest.

The Pig-nosed Turtle is active by day and night. For much of the day, it remains hidden in litter on the river bed or beneath a log, or it might flick sand up over its carapace (top shell) to conceal itself. The fruit and leaves of riverside plants, such as figs, lilly pillies and pandanus, are the main components of its diet as they drop into the water. It also eats aquatic plants, insects, shrimps and fish.

Below, left and right: The Pig-nosed Turtle's unmistakable protruding nose and large flippers, unlike those of any other freshwater turtle, make it easy to identify.

the FACTS!

ALTHOUGH UNRECORDED in Australia until 1970, unmistakable Aboriginal rock art (below) of the Pig-nosed Turtle has adorned galleries in Kakadu National Park for thousands of years.

IAN MORRIS

WHEN PIG-NOSED TURTLES develop within their eggshell, they enter a period of torpor (sleep), until heavy rain or floodwater provides the trigger for them to hatch.

THE SAW-SHELLED TURTLE (*Wollumbinia latisternum*) is one of the few animals able to eat poisonous Cane Toads. It has been seen using its front claws to shred the skin of Cane Toads before devouring them, apparently without any ill effect.

Above: The huge Perentie belongs to the family Varanidae — monitor lizards.

Lizards
— all shapes & sizes

Order: Squamata **Suborder:** Sauria
Families: Gekkonidae, Pygopodidae, Agamidae, Scincidae & Varanidae

Lizards are familiar animals to most Australians — they often live in our houses and backyards. In northern Australia, the Northern Dtella (Gehyra australis) sprawls on the fly screen after dark, or darts upside down across the ceiling to take refuge behind picture frames. In eastern Australia's largest cities, sun-loving Garden Skinks (Lampropholis guichenoti) lay their white eggs beneath broken plant pots and bask among the weeds in suburban gardens.

Above: Eastern Dtellas grow to around 12 cm long and cling effortlessly to walls.

Above: Male Red-sided Rainbow Skinks (*Carlia rufilatus*) change colour in the breeding season.

the FACTS!

THERE ARE APPROXIMATELY 4 796 species of lizard in the world, more than all the other reptiles combined.

IN AUSTRALIA, LIZARDS are particularly diverse, accounting for 75% of reptile species.

THE PERENTIE (*Varanus giganteus*), a monitor lizard, is Australia's largest lizard. A fully grown Perentie measures 2.4 m and weighs 15 kg.

THE KOMODO DRAGON (*Varanus komodoensis*) of Indonesia, is the world's largest lizard, growing to over 3 m and weighing as much as 125 kg!

A FEW SMALL SKINKS and geckoes vie for the honour of being Australia's smallest lizard, including the Top End Dwarf Skink (*Menetia alanae*), which is fully grown at just 7 cm.

Below: The surreal-looking Thorny Devil (*Moloch horridus*) is far from typical. It relies on its unusual body shape and excellent camouflage to deter predators.

TYPICAL REPTILES — OR ARE THEY?

With their blinking eyes, dry scaly bodies, strong claws and long tails, lizards are what we expect a reptile to look like; however, not all lizards fit this description. Some have a fixed, transparent scale covering the eye, like snakes. Others have no visible limbs.

Limb loss has evolved in two separate families of Australian lizards: legless lizards and skinks. Limb degeneration is most advanced in legless lizards, which are almost snake-like in appearance and movement. Legless lizards probably evolved from geckoes, and share a number of characteristics that add weight to this argument. Both geckoes and legless lizards lay two eggs per clutch, protrude their tongues to clean their eyes, have a "voice" (a feature confined to these families), and readily discard their tails when seized. However, no gecko, living or fossil, shows any sign of elongation or limb reduction, so we can only speculate how geckoes became legless lizards.

Although they lack legs, legless skinks are not snake-like; instead they move with a motion best described as a wriggle. We know how skinks lost their legs because they have left an easy trail to follow in the genus *Lerista* (sliders). Among its 80 members are surface-dwellers with well-developed limbs, each with five toes and (at the other end of the scale) elongate, limbless burrowers. Between the two extremes, a series of species demonstrate gradual limb degeneration and body elongation. Limb degeneration begins at the front. None have more toes on the forelimbs than the hindlimbs, and none posses forelimbs without hindlimbs.

Conservation Watch

The future of most Australian lizards will be assured, provided adequate areas of natural habitat are set aside and feral animals are controlled in these areas.

THE SACRIFICIAL TAIL

When seized, some lizards can voluntarily cast off their tails (a process known as autotomy), sometimes even when the tail itself is not grasped. This is a clever defence strategy employed by legless lizards, geckoes and most skinks. Once separated from the rest of the lizard, the tail jerks and twists with a mind of its own, distracting the attacker momentarily while the now-tailless lizard makes its escape. Over time, a replacement tail grows from the lizard's "stump", although it usually differs in length, shape, colour or texture from the original. Occasionally, tail regrowth may result in more than one tail sprouting from the fracture site! Some lizards are reluctant to part with their tails, but other species do so to such an extent that mature individuals rarely possess an original tail. Some geckoes have a single fracture point at the base of the tail and must shed the entire tail, but others can break the tail at any point along its length and concede only part of the tail to escape the grasp of a predator. Predators are not always responsible. Tail loss may also result from territorial fighting between members of the same species. Monitors and dragons cannot throw off their tails at all; however, some dragons are capable of partial tail regrowth if their tails are accidentally severed.

COLOUR CHANGE

Some lizards are able to change their skin colour in response to environmental conditions or to blend in with a background. Many dragon lizards also change colour in response to temperature variation or stress. At night, or when on pale surfaces, some geckoes lose all trace of colour and pattern, becoming white and translucent. They do this using chromatophores — cells beneath the skin that contain pigment and light-reflecting properties — and cell signalling (hormonal or neurotransmitted messages that instruct chromatophore cells to change colour in response to mood, stress or lighting).

The process of animals being able to modify their chromatophore cells slightly to mimic the colour of a background is known as "background adaptation". Most can only make small changes to their colour, but others, such as the Chameleon, can rapidly change through a numbers of hues. Seasonal colour change also occurs in dragon lizards and rainbow skinks (*Carlia*) during the mating season, when males develop bright colours to advertise their presence and ward off rival males.

Below: A Northern Dtella adopts pale colouring at night, becoming almost transparent.

Above: The tiny Top End Dwarf Skink is one of the smallest Australian lizards.

the FACTS!

SOME LIZARDS are able to store more than half the reserves of their body fat in their tails. If these lizards throw off their tails, they may be vulnerable to starvation.

THERE IS ANOTHER DOWNSIDE to a lizard losing its tail. Research indicates that, in some species, lizards that are missing some or all of their tails are slower than fully tailed members of the same species and become exhausted more quickly when running.

SOME GECKOES in the genus *Strophurus* scare off predators by squirting a sticky, foul-smelling liquid from their tails.

DIFFERENT LIZARDS LIVE for different periods of time, but usually the larger the lizard, the longer it lives. Some small lizards have an average lifespan of just one year.

Geckoes
— noisy night-hunters

Order: Squamata **Suborder:** Sauria
Family: Gekkonidae

Below: Juvenile Marbled Velvet Geckoes *(Oedura marmorata)* have distinct white bands compared to the spotted and banded adults.

STEVE PARISH

Geckoes are typically small, nocturnal lizards that sometimes share human dwellings. They occur throughout much of the world and are most abundant in tropical and subtropical regions. Some geckoes have excelled as travellers, colonising far-flung islands of the Pacific Ocean.

GECKOES (OR THEIR EGGS) reach new locations across the sea by "rafting" — hitching a ride in a crevice of a large log or among a mat of floating vegetation. In more recent times, their movements have been greatly assisted by humans, with many geckoes now travelling first class, concealed in the cargo carried by ships or aeroplanes.

Some of the most successful colonisers are able to reproduce parthenogenetically, which means without male participation. This means that when a female lands at an isolated location, she does not have to rely on the slim chance that a male has also arrived to found a new population.

STEVE PARISH

the FACTS!

THE NAME "GECKO" is thought to be derived from an imitation of a gecko's call.

GECKOES MAY APPEAR to have soft velvety skin, but their bodies are actually covered in tiny scales. Some even have coarse skin, studded with small spines or tubercles.

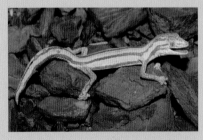

Above: This agitated White-striped Gecko *(Strophurus taeniatus)* has produced beads of sticky, liquid from the pores on its tail. Should it be seized, it will smear the noxious substance onto its attacker.

A COMMONLY SEEN INVADER

The Asian House Gecko *(Hemidactylus frenatus)* is a native of south-east Asia, but has now become the common house gecko of northern Australian cities and towns and has even spread as far as north Africa and the USA. In Australia, it is confined to human settlements and does not inhabit native bushland. When a house or building is abandoned, the Asian House Gecko soon disappears, suggesting that it relies on humans — or at least on electric lights that attract bugs and moths after dark — for its survival. In the suburbs of Darwin, in the Northern Territory, the more aggressive Asian House Gecko displaced the Northern Dtella *(Gehyra australis)* as the common house gecko over a period of about 30 years. However, in Darwin's rural areas, where houses are surrounded by native bushland, the Northern Dtella still maintains its position as the dominant and most commonly seen house gecko.

STEVE PARISH

NIGHT-TIME FORAGERS

In Australia, geckoes are most diverse in northern Australia and the arid central regions. Few species live in the temperate south-east and south-west. Because geckoes are active at night (nocturnal), they are particularly suited to tropical climates, where warm night-time temperatures enable them to forage for insects throughout most of the year. In cooler temperate regions, geckoes might not feed for six months of the year. To survive in New Zealand's cold climate, the unique green geckoes *(Naultinus* spp.) are active during the day (diurnal) and give birth to living young.

Conservation Watch

Six species of Banded-tailed Geckoes (*Phyllurus* spp.), such as the Southern Banded-tailed Gecko (*Phyllurus caudiannulatus,* right) are each confined to small, isolated pockets of elevated forest in eastern Queensland. Climate change has the potential to threaten their survival.

DEFYING GRAVITY

How geckoes climb a glass window pane or scuttle upside down across the ceiling, has both amazed and puzzled people for generations. However, recent studies have shed some light on how they do it. The adhesive pads beneath the toes of many gecko species are covered with very fine, densely packed, hair-like structures (setae), each of which branches at the tip into hundreds of even finer structures called spatulae. A gecko has millions of setae beneath its feet and they are so small, that an electron microscope is needed to see them. A weak "molecular attractive force" called van der Waals force operates between the setae and the surface, and this force holds the gecko firmly in place.

LARGEST GECKO

Australia's largest gecko, the Ring-tailed Gecko (*Cyrtodactylus tuberculatus*), grows to a total length of 30 cm, but most geckoes are much smaller.

The Ring-tailed Gecko occurs in rocky locations in vine forest and rainforest on Cape York Peninsula, Queensland. It also occurs in New Guinea, but the relationship between the two races is not fully understood and the Australian population may well be a different species. The Ring-tailed Gecko occasionally lives on the exterior walls of buildings in rural locations and also in sheds and abandoned dwellings.

Right: The Ring-tailed Gecko, at 30 cm long, dwarfs some of its gecko cousins.

MICHAEL CERMAK

the FACTS!

A GECKO DISENGAGES its toes by uncurling them away from the surface, backwards from the tip, which is a very unusual way of walking. As it runs across a wall, the pads are engaged and disengaged about 15 times per second.

THE ADHESIVE PADS of a gecko's toes stick to any surface, clean or dirty, wet or dry, rough or smooth. They are self-cleaning.

SCIENTISTS ARE STUDYING the remarkable adhesive quality of the gecko's toe pad (below) with the aim of duplicating it in a commercial adhesive that could be used in car braking systems. One scientist at a university in Oregon, USA, believes this "gecko glue" is so powerful that one-third of a square metre of the substance could stop a car travelling at 80 km/h in just 5 m!

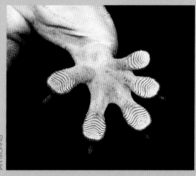

IAN MORRIS

HARMLESS, BUT FULL OF PUFF

All geckoes are completely harmless, but some species, such as the Thick-tailed Gecko (*Underwoodisaurus milii,* left) — also called the Barking Gecko — put on quite a show when threatened. Arching its inflated body on fully extended limbs and with its mouth opened wide, the Thick-tailed Gecko launches a mock counterattack, all the while making a "barking" noise. When such behaviour is directed towards a human, it appears rather comical, but the impact on a predator contemplating the gecko as its next meal might well determine its fate.

Left: The Thick-tailed Gecko barks and bluffs its way out of danger.

Below: Eastern Spiny-tailed Geckoes employ a "tail squirting" defensive tactic.

TAIL SQUIRTERS

When harassed, the Eastern Spiny-tailed Gecko (*Strophurus williamsi*) not only lifts its tail, makes high-pitched chirping sounds and opens its mouth to expose the deep purplish-blue interior, it also uses a messier defensive strategy. The Eastern Spiny-tailed Gecko is one of a group of geckoes in the genus *Strophurus* that squirt or smear a noxious, syrupy liquid from glands on the tail onto an attacker. The irritating liquid forms into sticky strands and, when repeatedly squirted, may overwhelm a predator. Some "tail-squirters" can eject their noxious filaments for a distance of 30 cm. Because its tail is so crucial to its defence, the Eastern Spiny-tailed Gecko, like all members of its genus, is very reluctant to shed its tail.

the FACTS!

AUSTRALIAN GECKOES have an immovable, transparent scale protecting the eye, which they regularly clean by licking with their protruding broad tongues. Snakes, legless lizards and some skinks also possess this fixed eye covering, but only geckoes and legless lizards use their tongues like "windscreen wipers" in this fashion.

GECKOES HAVE DISTINCTIVE toes that vary in shape and structure. Some have claws, others have adhesive pads and many have a combination of both claws and pads.

THE SCIENTIFIC NAMES of many geckoes reflect the importance of the toes in their classification. *Diplodactylus*, for instance, means "double-toe", *Lepidodactylus*, "scaly-toe" and *Cyrtodactylus*, "curved-toe".

Below: The swollen tail of the Marbled Velvet Gecko provides a fat store for the gecko during lean times.

Above, top to bottom: Centralian Prickly Knob-tailed Gecko (*Nephrurus amyae*); Fat-tailed Gecko (*Diplodactylus conspicillatus*); Helmeted Gecko (*Diplodactylus galeatus*).

Right: Hammer-tailed Gecko (*Underwoodisaurus sphyrurus*)

TAILS IN ALL TYPES AND SHAPES

Gecko tails come in a wide variety of shapes and sizes. Some have rows of spines, others may be leaf-shaped, turnip-shaped or long and tapering. The very short tail of the Eastern Prickly Knob-tailed Gecko (*Nephrurus asper*) has a small sphere at its tip, the function of which is unknown. Of course, this already stumpy-tailed species does not discard its tail.

The Fat-tailed Gecko (*Diplodactylus conspicillatus*) prefers to shelter in the vertical shaft of an abandoned spider burrow and uses its squat tail to form a tight-fitting plug. In sealing the burrow, the Fat-tailed Gecko maintains optimum temperature and humidity levels within its retreat. The tail also provides a barrier against some predators. A small snake entering the spider hole in search of a meal might be thwarted, but not a goanna, which will dig the gecko out with its strong claws.

STEVE PARISH

Right: The Eungella Banded-tailed Gecko (*Phyllurus nepthys*) is excellently adapted for sheltering beneath bark or on tree trunks.

STEVE PARISH

Conservation Watch

The Pernatty Knob-tailed Gecko (*Nephrurus deleani*) is found only on sand dunes near Pernatty Lagoon, South Australia. Captive breeding programs can help ensure the survival of rare lizards.

GECKO HABITATS

Geckoes are either terrestrial (ground-dwelling) or arboreal (tree-dwelling). They spend the daylight hours in burrows, soil cracks, beneath rocks, logs or bark on the ground, in rock crevices, under loose bark of standing trees, or in tree hollows. The Southern Spotted Velvet Gecko (*Oedura tryoni*) shelters beneath loose bark, or in a rock crevice, depending on the availability of either habitat. Jean's Striped Geckoes (*Strophurus jeanae*) live exclusively in dense spinifex grass clumps, where their colour and striped pattern provide a very effective camouflage among the needles of the spinifex.

Some small geckoes choose to shelter in disused spider burrows. The Southern Leaf-tailed Gecko (*Saltuarius swaini*) lives on large trees in the rainforest. During the day, it hides under loose bark, or in a hollow of the tree. It forages on the tree at night and with its olive colour and mottled pattern, is very difficult to detect on the lichen-encrusted tree trunk.

MICHAEL CERMAK

Above: The Chameleon Gecko (*Carphodactylus laevis*) is the sole member of its genus and inhabits rainforest in Queensland's Wet Tropics.

the FACTS!

AUSTRALIA PRESENTLY HAS 112 described gecko species. They range across Australia, excluding cool climates such as Tasmania, the Alps and the far south-eastern mainland.

THE VARIEGATED DTELLA (*Gehyra variegata*) lays a single egg per clutch. The egg may weigh up to 30% of the female's body weight!

TO SUPPLEMENT its insectivorous diet, the Northern Dtella (*Gehyra australis*) climbs into acacia trees and licks oozing sap.

Above: In addition to toe pads, the Arnhem Land Cave Gecko (*Pseudothecadactylus lindneri*) has an adhesive pad beneath the tail tip.

GECKO GRUB

Geckoes feed mostly on insects and arthropods, such as spiders and scorpions; however, large species, such as the Western Smooth Knob-tailed Gecko (*Nephrurus levis occidentalis*, below) also include smaller geckoes and skinks in their diet.

ONLY TWO EGGS

All Australian geckoes lay eggs and the clutch almost always consists of two rather large eggs. An exception is the widespread Variegated Dtella (*Gehyra variegata*), which lays only one very large egg at a time.

Above: The Jewelled Gecko (*Strophurus elderi*) dwells only in clumps of spinifex grass.

STEVE PARISH

Legless lizards
— snake look-alikes

Order: Squamata **Suborder:** Sauria
Family: Pygopodidae

Legless lizards are often mistaken for snakes, due to their snake-like movements and appearance. Looking like a snake is not always a good thing because many of these harmless reptiles are unnecessarily killed.

STILL VERY MUCH A LIZARD

Legless lizards (sometimes also called flap-footed lizards) are long and snake-like with no external trace of front limbs. The hindlimbs have been reduced to small flaps, which are not usually noticed, because they are held firmly against the body.

A legless lizard's similarity to a snake is superficial — closer inspection reveals many significant differences. A legless lizard's body is less flexible than that of a snake and its tail is much longer and is readily cast off if the lizard is seized by a predator. Regenerated tails are common among legless lizards, but snakes cannot cast off their tails or regrow them if they are severed. Unlike the slender, forked tongue of a snake, the tongue of a legless lizard is broad and flat. Remnant hindlimbs are present in all legless lizards; however, among snakes, only pythons possess tiny remnant hindlimb structures in the form of small spurs on either side of the vent. The majority of legless lizards also have visible ear openings, whereas snakes have no external trace of ears.

the FACTS!

38 LEGLESS LIZARD SPECIES inhabit Australia, with one common species, Burton's Snake-lizard (*Lialis burtonis*, above) also found in New Guinea. Legless lizards are endemic to Australia and New Guinea and occur nowhere else on Earth!

THE LIMBLESS CONDITION is not confined to legless lizards; the skink family also includes limbless species. The flap-like hindlimb is too small to be of any use in most legless lizards, although the larger "flap-foot" possessed by members of the genus *Pygopus* is sometimes extended to help them manoeuvre in dense vegetation.

AS ITS NAME IMPLIES, the Red-tailed Worm-lizard (*Aprasia inaurita*) has a red tip on its tail, which it raises from the ground when alarmed.

THE TAIL of the Single-striped Delma (*Delma labialis*) measures four times its body length.

MIMICKING A SNAKE

The head pattern of some legless lizards, such as the Eastern Hooded Scaly-foot (*Pygopus schraderi*, below), is similar to that of some venomous snakes of a similar size. When confronted, the Eastern Hooded Scaly-foot appears to mimic the threatening behaviour of a snake, raising its forebody and flicking out its tongue. Resembling or copying the behaviour of an unrelated but dangerous species is known as "Batesian mimicry".

LEGLESS GECKO KIN

There are no intermediate forms between legless lizards and geckoes, either among living species, or in the fossil record, but it is clear that legless lizards evolved from geckoes and therefore share some similarities in anatomy and behaviour. Some scientists even consider legless lizards to be merely legless members of the gecko family. Like geckoes, they utter squeaking sounds and have a fixed eye shield that they clean by protruding the tongue. They also always lay just two eggs per clutch and are able to cast off their tails without hesitation when seized. For many legless lizards, the original tail is much longer than the body — sometimes making up 80% of the lizard's total length — so shedding the tail can dramatically shorten the lizard's length.

Above: Eastern Hooded Scaly-foot (*Pygopus schraderi*)

Above: The Single-striped Delma (*Delma labialis*) is one of the largest legless lizards in its genus, growing to an average length of 50 cm.

WHERE THEY LIVE

All legless lizards are terrestrial, but some climb into low shrubs or grass clumps to bask. Some species burrow in loose soil beneath leaf litter, others shelter within dense vegetation, or beneath rocks and logs lying on the soil. The burrowing, worm-lizards (*Aprasia*) are very secretive and rarely observed in the open. In accordance with their burrowing lifestyle, they have glossy scales and, with the exception of one species, no visible ear opening. Most legless lizards are either active during the day, or at night, depending on prevailing temperature. The wide-ranging Burton's Snake-lizard (*Lialis burtonis*) is usually nocturnal in arid and tropical Australia, or most active during the day in temperate regions.

the FACTS!

WHEN ALARMED, the slender, limbless Excitable Delma (*Delma tincta*, above) frantically makes a series of erratic "jumping" movements to try and quickly reach the nearest ground cover.

THE WESTERN HOODED SCALY-FOOT (*Pygopus nigriceps*) executes a "death roll" after seizing a large spider or scorpion in an effort to disorientate its prey.

BURTON'S SNAKE-LIZARDS (below) can differ in colour and pattern; they may be cream, yellowish, fawn, brown, reddish or grey. Some have highly contrasting facial stripes, or stripes extending the full length of the body and tail.

Above: The attractively patterned Southern Scaly-foot crushes large spiders in its jaws and dines off their body juices.

A LEGLESS LIZARD'S LUNCH

Legless lizards eat insects, spiders and their eggsacs, as well as scorpions. Some fruit and nectar is also included in their diet. The Southern Scaly-foot (*Pygopus lepidopodus*) preys on large spiders. When too big to swallow whole, a spider is repeatedly bitten and beaten against the ground. The Southern Scaly-foot then laps up the juices from the spider's crumpled body. One very different legless lizard, Burton's Snake-lizard preys on lizards (including other legless lizards) and occasionally small snakes. It is equipped with snake-like, recurved teeth to grip the smooth bodies of skinks, which are its usual prey.

THE BRIGALOW SCALY-FOOT (*Paradelma orientalis*) has been observed climbing up wattle tree trunks and researchers believe this may be so it can lick up the sap.

Dragons
— alert & swift

Order: Squamata   **Suborder:** Sauria
Family: Agamidae

Dragons are widespread and flamboyant lizards that are renowned as the exhibitionists of the reptile world. Most lizards are secretive, but dragons typically take up prominent positions out in the open and sometimes engage in elaborate displays or bluff defences if disturbed.

Above: A mature male Painted Dragon is more colourful than a female.

the FACTS!

THE JACKY LIZARD
(*Amphibolurus muricatus*) was one of the first Australian reptiles recorded. It was described by English zoologist George Shaw in *Journal of a Voyage to New South Wales*, published in 1790.

SOME SMALL DRAGONS, such as the Painted Dragon (*Ctenophorus pictus,* top) have a lifespan of just one year and rarely live to see two summers.

THE MALE RED-BARRED
Dragon *(Ctenophorus vadnappa, below),* has spectacular red, blue and yellow colouring and is one of Australia's most attractive lizards. In comparison, the female Red-barred Dragon is much duller, with just a simple, speckled brown pattern.

MYTHICAL DRAGONS IN MINIATURE

Typical dragon features are moveable eyelids, four-clawed, well-developed limbs and a long tapering tail. While none of them breathe fire, it is easy to see why they received the name "dragon" because some of them have impressive enlarged spines and a crest running down the back, as well as an extendable throat pouch (known as a gular pouch). When combined with a threatening posture, this dramatic adornment helps dragons deter predators or frighten off rival males. Over the rest of the body, the rough, loose skin gathers in folds, particularly on the throat and sides of the body, and is also often studded with conical scales.

BIZARRE BEHAVIOUR

Dragons use what, to us, seems like bizarre signalling behaviour during social interaction and for defensive purposes. This signalling, including head nodding and forearm waving, reaches its peak in the breeding season during confrontations between rival males.

SEXUALLY DIMORPHIC

In contrast to most lizards, male and female dragons vary considerably in appearance. Males are usually larger, more spinose and more vibrantly coloured than females. Dragons can also change their colour to suit their environment.

Below: During the breeding season, the male Yellow-sided Two-lined Dragon (*Diporiphora magna*), on the left, becomes much more colourful than the female, on the right.

Conservation Watch

The Grassland Earless Dragon (*Tympanocryptis pinguicolla*) occurs in scattered remnant pockets of native grassland, from Victoria to south-eastern Queensland, although it has not been sighted in Victoria since the 1960s and may be locally extinct.

TA-TA LIZARD

Gilbert's Dragons (*Amphibolurus gilberti*) are known as Ta-Ta Lizards (as in waving goodbye) because they nod their head and wave their forearms when approached. Why it chooses to draw attention to itself in this way is not fully understood, but it is perhaps conveying the message, "Here I am, but don't waste energy chasing me, because I am faster than you". Gilbert's Dragons are indeed very fast lizards!

MALE SHOW-OFFS

Most dragons are fiercely territorial, especially breeding males, which signal their dominance by displaying bold and often vividly contrasting colours. The male's splendid displays are less about attracting the attention of females, and more about intimidating other males and driving them from his territory. During the breeding season, a territorial male "shows off" by perching in a prominent position to display his colours to maximum effect. Of course, being so conspicuous increases his chances of being noticed by a predator, but this is a risk he is prepared to take to keep control of his territory and mate with the resident females.

Males of many species also combine their vibrancy with complex threatening behaviour designed to drive other males away. At the approach of a rival male, a dominant male may turn side on, broaden his lateral (side) aspect, lower his gular (throat) pouch, raise the crests on his neck and back, lift his tail into a coil and move the rear of his body up and down, as if doing "push-ups"!

HEAT-TOLERANT REPTILES

Australian dragons are most abundant in the continent's dry heartland, where they are more able than most lizards to tolerate the very high temperatures. Their eyelids, both top and bottom, have prominent hoods to help shield the eyes from the sun, however, even with these adaptations, most need to seek shelter in the heat of a summer's day. The Canegrass Two-lined Dragon (*Diporiphora winneckei*) has a different strategy for keeping its body temperature down at this hottest part of the day. It sits vertically, clinging to the very top of a narrow spinifex grass stalk, exposing very little of its body surface to the overhead sun while catching any cooling airflows.

Above: Gilbert's Dragons are common in some suburban areas, and their eye-catching behaviour makes them easy to spot.

the FACTS!

SOME DRAGONS that live in arid regions rarely drink surface water; instead they get their moisture from the insects and plants they eat or from the dew.

THE THORNY DEVIL (*Moloch horridus*) is an arid-adapted dragon that drinks simply by standing in a puddle! Water is soaked up by "capillary action" (passive movement of liquid in a tube or channel) and moves from the limbs, along a network of fine channels between the scales, to the corners of the mouth. The Thorny Devil also collects water from condensation on its spines, from drops of rainwater that fall on its body or by standing in wet sand.

MANY ARBOREAL DRAGONS, including the Burns' Dragon (*Amphibolurus burnsi*), sleep on exposed branches on warm summer nights.

Left: Perching on the top of flora in hot weather helps the Canegrass Two-lined Dragon stay cool.

Right: The sentinel-like stance of this Eyrean Earless Dragon (*Tympanocryptis tetraporophora*) is actually its way of keeping cool by moving its body away from a hot rock surface.

Above: The Long-nosed Water Dragon (*Amphibolurus longirostris*) is primarily arboreal and frequently perches on vegetation.

IAN MORRIS

PERCH & POUNCE

Although most dragons are terrestrial, many are also excellent climbers and some species, especially rainforest inhabitants such as Boyd's Forest Dragon (*Hypsilurus boydii*), spend much of the time in trees and bushes. Those which prefer life on the ground sometimes dig burrows in the soil or take over the abandoned burrows of other animals. Some also shelter in the crevices of rocky outcrops. To enable them to keep a keen eye on insect food in their surrounding environments, both terrestrial and arboreal dragons seek out high vantage points so they can survey the surrounding area, watching for the movement of insects. Ants are an important component of the diet of many small species, while larger species will also tackle larger animals such as nestling birds and small mammals.

the FACTS!

ABOUT 70 species of dragon are currently recognised in Australia.

DRAGONS CAN ALTER their colour in response to climatic or emotional cues, in some cases rapidly and dramatically. When they need to increase their rate of heat absorption, they become darker in colour. They grow lighter when they need to reduce their body heat.

THE NORTHERN Water Dragon (*Amphibolurus temporalis*) is often seen in well-watered parks in the suburbs of Darwin, Northern Territory. In fact, it is more common in artificial habitat than in surrounding bushland, where is it restricted to river banks and creeks.

FOR YEARS, the courtyard of a crowded suburban shopping mall in Maroochydore, Queensland, supported a population of Eastern Water Dragons living around a fountain and artificial creek. Eastern Water Dragons are often very shy, but these lizards calmly basked within metres of shoppers.

THE EASTERN WATER DRAGON swims like a crocodile, with its limbs pressed against the sides of its body. Propulsion is provided by sideways tail movement.

RIVER BANK REGULARS

The semi-aquatic Water Dragon (*Physignathus lesueurii*) is the sole Australian member of its genus, and includes two subspecies. Both of them enjoy a "riparian" lifestyle, living both on land and in water, basking on the banks of rivers or creeks. The Eastern Water Dragon subspecies (*P. l. lesueurii*) is a large, conspicuous lizard that is common and widespread in eastern Australia. It rarely strays far from the water and makes its presence known as it drops from overhanging tree branches into the water with a loud splash. It swims underwater to emerge on the opposite bank, but may remain submerged for as long as 90 minutes! The Gippsland Water Dragon (*P. l. howittii*) ranges from Gippsland, Victoria, to Kangaroo Valley in New South Wales. Water Dragons are omnivorous and consume insects, frogs, small lizards, fish and crustaceans, as well as fallen fruits and flowers.

Above, right: Bennett's Two-lined Dragon (*Diporiphora bennettii*) surveys the scene.

Right: Eastern Water Dragons are secretive, arboreal and semi-aquatic. They quickly leap into the water if threatened so often the only sign of them is a loud "splash".

MICHAEL CERMACK

Above: Thorny Devils are active by day, often during cloudy weather.

LIKE A CLOCKWORK TOY

The bizarre Thorny Devil (*Moloch horridus*), with its mass of conical spines, is a unique and unmistakeable lizard. It occurs widely throughout arid Australia, where it moves slowly across desert dunes with a stop-start motion, not unlike that of a clockwork toy. Despite its name and bristling appearance, it is a placid and harmless lizard that feeds solely on small, but aggressive ants in the genus *Iridomyrmex*. At each meal, it may consume up to 5 000 ants, with a methodical flicking of its tongue. The function of the large, spiny hump on the back of the Thorny Devil's neck is not fully understood, but it possibly acts as a decoy, resembling a false head when the lizard dips its head in a defensive posture.

BEARDED DRAGONS

Australia has six species of bearded dragons that collectively occur throughout most of the continent. They are easily recognised by their spiny gular (throat) pouch or "beard" which is extended, combined with a gaping mouth, when the lizard is threatened. The Dwarf Bearded Dragon (*Pogona minor*) is one of the smaller species, growing to around 35 cm in length. It has a poorly developed beard, so rather than present its beard when threatened, it prefers to retreat into a dense shrub.

Like all dragons, bearded dragons have keen eyesight that is particularly attuned to movement. Some, such as the Eastern Bearded Dragon (*Pogona barbata*, right), supplement their insectivorous diet with flowers and other vegetation. Typically, they feed by perching on top of a fence post or tree stump and then descending to the ground when the movement of an insect catches their eye.

the FACTS!

SOME SMALL DRAGONS lay only 2–3 parchment-shelled eggs, but the large Eastern Bearded Dragon (*Pogona barbata*) may lay as many as 35 in a clutch!

Below: A Pebble Earless Dragon (*Tympanocryptis cephalus*) crouches motionless amongst stones to avoid detection.

Above: The Ring-tailed Dragon (*Ctenophorus caudicinctus*) varies greatly in colour depending on its sex, age and distribution. There are six subspecies ranging across central and western Australia.

Below: The Mitchell's Bearded Dragon (*Pogona mitchelli*) is one of the smallest of the bearded dragons, reaching around 32 cm.

Above: The startling shock tactics of the Frilled Lizard. *Top, left to right:* "Frillies" perch motionless on a tree trunk, hoping to remain unseen; If alarmed they quickly extend their frill as a defensive action.

the FACTS!

A FRILLED LIZARD'S paper-thin frill is supported by narrow rods of cartilage that work something like the ribs in an umbrella. They are connected to the jaw muscles and automatically spread the frill when the mouth is opened widely. When fully erect, the frill of a large Frilled Lizard can measure 30 cm across!

THE FRILLED LIZARD is the sole member of the genus *Chlamydosaurus,* which means "caped lizard".

DRAGONS ARE CONSIDERED strictly diurnal, but some small dragons, such as the Pebble Earless Dragon (*Tympanocryptis cephalus,* below), have been observed active after dark.

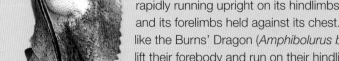

THE SPECTACULAR FRILLED DRAGON

Australia's Frilled Lizard (*Chlamydosaurus kingii*) — called the "blanket lizard" by Aborigines of western Arnhem Land — is probably the world's most spectacular dragon. When threatened, it produces a remarkable defensive display. With its mouth wide open, displaying the bright yellow interior, and its erect frill fully encircling the head, it stands on its hindlimbs, rocking from side to side while hissing loudly. A frightened Frilled Lizard will make short lunges towards its tormentor and is capable of inflicting a serious bite with its powerful jaws. When not erect, the impressive frill sits folded back over the chest and shoulders. If it cannot bluff its attacker into retreat, the Frilled Lizard flees, rapidly running upright on its hindlimbs, with its tail lifted and its forelimbs held against its chest. Other dragons, like the Burns' Dragon (*Amphibolurus burnsi*), also lift their forebody and run on their hindlimbs. Using this method, they are capable of very fast speeds and can quickly distance themselves from a predator.

EARLESS DRAGONS

Australia has eight species of earless dragons in the genus *Tympanocryptis*, and as their name suggests, all of them have no trace of an external ear. They also lack a functional ear drum, or tympanum, but even without this they are still able to hear to varying degrees (mostly low frequency and very loud sounds). Strangely, the Grassland Earless Dragon (*Tympanocryptis pinguicolla*) is one of just two dragon species to make true vocalisations (noises other than hissing). Along with another species in the same genus, it has been recorded making squeaking sounds when handled. Unfortunately habit destruction across much of its limited range in Victoria, New South Wales and Queensland has put this species on the endangered list.

Most earless dragons are well camouflaged in the environments they prefer. The Pebble Earless Dragon (*Tympanocryptis cephalus,* left) has a particularly effective camouflage strategy. It crouches motionless among scattered stones, where its squat body resembles a pebble and its narrow tail, often held at an angle to the body, resembles a twig.

RIGHT & FAR RIGHT: STEVE PARISH

Conservation Watch

In the 1960s the Frilled Lizard (*Chlamydosaurus kingii*) was common around Brisbane, but it is now very rare in this area. It has succumbed to clearing of bushland and predation by domestic dogs and cats.

Far left to left: The colourful Southern Forest Dragon; Boyd's Forest Dragon blends in well with its surroundings.

COLOURFUL BUT WELL CAMOUFLAGED

Some dragons are brightly coloured attention-seekers, but most are just as good at hiding as they are at attracting attention to themselves. The Southern Forest Dragon (*Hypsilurus spinipes*) inhabits rainforest in north-eastern New South Wales and south-eastern Queensland, where its olive colour and mottled pattern provide excellent camouflage on the lichen-covered saplings on which it rests. If approached, it remains stationary or slowly creeps around to the other side of the sapling to avoid detection. The slow-moving Boyd's Forest Dragon (*Hypsilurus boydii*) inhabits rainforest in north Queensland. Spotted facial markings and spectacular, spiny crests on its throat, neck and back, help it blend in with the tree trunks and branches. Like the Southern Forest Dragon, it remains motionless and relies on a cryptic pattern to avoid predators.

STEVE PARISH

Above: Central Netted Dragons (*Ctenophorus nuchalis*) prefer to live in shallow burrows in arid regions.

CHAMELEON-LIKE

As the sole member of its genus, the distinctive, slow-moving Chameleon Dragon (*Chelosania brunnea*) is unlike other dragons. It shares some behavioural and physical similarities with chameleons, a family of lizards inhabiting Africa, Asia and southern Europe. However despite its name and superficial similarities, the Chameleon Dragon is not closely related to chameleons. Instead, the likeness between the two is an example of convergent evolution — when unrelated animals independently develop the same (or similar) characteristics to adapt to the same environmental pressures. The Chameleon Dragon is a rarely encountered lizard that inhabits the Top End of the Northern Territory and the Kimberley region of Western Australia. It remains motionless and hidden in a shrub when approached, so it is often easily overlooked.

TWO-LINED DRAGONS

Fourteen species of two-lined dragons in the genus *Diporiphora* occur throughout northern and central Australia. They are common, often colourful lizards, the males of which often take up prominent perches on rocks, stumps and termite mounds. Males and females vary considerably in colour and pattern, but all generally have two stripes running down the back, from which they receive their common name.

Most of them occur in Australia's north, although two, the Plain-backed Two-lined Dragon (*Diporiphora reginae*) and the Pink Two-line Dragon (*Diporiphora linga*) occur in southern Western Australia and South Australia respectively. One, the unusually named Tommy Roundhead (*Diporiphora australis,* below) is common to Queensland's east coast.

the FACTS!

IN WESTERN Queensland and New South Wales, some people call the small colourful dragons that are common to these regions "Carnies" — a nickname for flamboyant carnival showmen.

TASMANIA HAS only one dragon species, the cold-tolerant, Mountain Dragon (*Rankinia diemensis*).

THE CRESTED DRAGON (*Ctenophorus cristatus*) is also known as the "Bicycle Lizard". It runs very quickly on its hindlimbs, with its forebody raised, making the rapid movement of its hindlimbs resemble a pedalling motion.

STEVE PARISH

Monitors
— the largest lizards

Order: Squamata   **Suborder:** Sauria
Family: Varanidae

"Goannas", more formally known as monitor lizards, are Australia's largest and most conspicuous lizards, however some members of the same family are smaller and less commonly seen. All of them belong to a single genus, Varanus — of which there are around 58 worldwide members ranging from Africa to Asia, the western Pacific and Australia.

the FACTS!

A LIST OF AUSTRALIAN lizards in order of size would feature monitors in the top nine places (including the Perentie as the biggest).

MONITOR LIZARDS PROBABLY EVOLVED about 90 million years ago (during the Cretaceous Period) in the Northern Hemisphere. Later, during the Miocene Epoch, approximately 15 million years ago, they spread to Africa and, finally, to Australia, where 26 species occur. Their general body shape has changed little over millions of years.

THE AMPHIBIAN-EATING Yellow-spotted Monitor (*Varanus panoptes*) and Mertens' Water Monitor (*Varanus mertensi*), have been affected by the spread of the poisonous Cane Toad (*Bufo marinus*) across northern Australia.

IN AUSTRALIA, the bright-green and black Emerald Monitor *(Varanus prasinus)* is confined to several islands in the Torres Strait, although it is common and widespread in New Guinea.

MONITORING SURROUNDINGS

With 26 of the world's species, Australia is considered a stronghold of monitor diversity. Australian monitors range from 20 cm in length to more than 2 m and the genus includes the world's largest lizard, the Komodo Dragon (*Varanus komodoensis*). Some large species stand upright on their hindlimbs and tail to check (or monitor) their surroundings and it is from this habit that they get their name.

STANDING UPRIGHT IS also a way for these lizards to remain cool. By lifting its body and balancing on its hindlimbs and tail, a Yellow-spotted Monitor (above) is able to cool off by reducing body contact with the hot sand. The monitor also adopts this "tripod" stance to threaten an intruder or to give it a better view.

POWERFUL PREDATORS

Monitors are relentless day-time predators equipped with sharp, recurved, needle-like teeth. They will eat almost any animal small enough for them to swallow, including insects, spiders, fish, frogs, crustaceans, smaller reptiles (sometimes not that much smaller than themselves), birds and mammals.

A monitor typically swallows its prey whole with a rapid series of jerking, forward movements of the head. This ensures that the prey remains in the grip of the lizard's recurved teeth as it moves towards the throat. A large monitor might travel for more than a kilometre while foraging within its home range, stalking, digging up, or chasing down its prey.

SNAKE-LIKE TONGUES

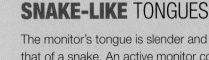

The monitor's tongue is slender and forked, like that of a snake. An active monitor constantly flicks out its tongue to catch airborne particles, which are transferred to an olfactory (smelling) organ (called Jacobson's organ) in the roof of its mouth. By protruding the tongue, a monitor is in effect "tasting" the air, to alert it to danger, or to track its prey.

STEVE PARISH

Above, left to right: Lace Monitors are strong climbers; Heath Monitor.

CARRION FEEDERS

As well as predators, large monitors are carrion feeders that are commonly seen feeding on animal carcasses beside the road or scavenging for scraps in picnic areas and rubbish tips.

In the Top End of the Northern Territory, picnic areas have "goanna-proof" rubbish bins to deter large Yellow-Spotted Monitors from climbing into them. Some particularly bold lizards create such a nuisance to the public, that they occasionally need to be captured and relocated by park rangers.

WHERE THEY LIVE

Monitors range across most of the continent apart from Tasmania, with the most widespread being the Sand Monitor (*Varanus gouldii*). Most are terrestrial, living in a burrow in the soil or within a rock crevice. Others prefer to shelter in tree hollows or beneath bark.

Some tropical species, such as the Mangrove Monitor (*Varanus indicus*) are semi-aquatic and live in dense vegetation beside rivers, creeks or estuaries, retreating to the water when approached.

the FACTS!

MANY MONITORS are particularly fond of eggs and frequently raid the nests of birds, turtles and crocodiles.

GOANNA IS NOT the Aboriginal name for these reptiles, but was probably given to these large lizards in error. It is believed to be a corruption of "iguana" — a name incorrectly applied to monitor lizards by early settlers.

SOME MONITORS are capable of extreme bursts of speed and can quickly distance themselves from any kind of threat. When in retreat, they often lift the forebody and run on their powerful hindlimbs alone, which is known as bipedal locomotion.

MOST LIZARDS struggle to run and breathe at the same time, as the same muscles needed to expand their lungs are used to move their bodies. However, researchers at Harvard University, USA, discovered that African Savannah Monitors (*Varanus exanthematicus*) use their throats like a "throat pump" to gulp in extra oxygen while running.

WHIP-LIKE TAILS

Monitors have movable eyelids, four strongly clawed limbs, loose skin covered with tough non-overlapping scales and generally a long, tapering tail. Some tree-dwelling species have prehensile tails (adapted for gripping), helping them to climb about in the treetops. Others, like the Spiny-tailed Monitor (*Varanus acanthurus*) use their tails for defence. The Spiny-tailed Monitor's robust tail, covered with hard spines and keels, is used to block the entrance to the crevice or burrow where it is sheltering. Some large species even swing the tail like a whip to defend themselves! Mitchell's Water Monitor (*Varanus mitchelli*, above) has a sideways flattened tail, that provides the thrust for swimming.

Above: The Spiny-tailed Monitor's tail is used as a "barricade" to its burrow.

Above: Juvenile Black-palmed Rock Monitors (*Varanus glebopalma*) have banded tails.

Right: Yellow-spotted Monitor (*Varanus panoptes*)

IAN MORRIS

Above: Freckled Monitors (*Varanus tristis orientalis*) are good climbers that take to the trees when alarmed.

the FACTS!

IN 2005, RESEARCHERS were amazed to find that monitor lizards are slightly venomous and are able to produce nine out of the ten toxins snakes are able to produce, as well as other unidentified toxins. The mild venom, designed to help monitors subdue their prey, is not dangerous to humans. The findings suggest that snakes and monitor lizards (as well as some other venomous lizards such as Bearded Dragons) probably share a common ancestor that lived approximately 200 million years ago.

Above: Yellow-spotted Monitors will stand their ground if approached, but most flee if their bluff fails to work.

ENEMIES & PREDATORS

Juvenile monitors are vulnerable to attack by many other animals, but an adult monitor has few natural enemies except for humans. Goannas are an important food source for Aborigines in many parts of the continent and are generally dug from their burrows, despatched with a blow to the head and cooked, skin and all, over hot coals. The skin is then peeled away and the white flesh, considered similar in taste to chicken, is eaten. Monitors usually retreat to a burrow or scuttle up trees if threatened, but they may fiercely defend themselves and can bite without hesitation when attacked. Their strong jaws and needle sharp teeth, can inflict a serious wound.

MACHO MALES

Males of large monitor species stand upright and grapple in combat during the breeding season. Their main objective appears to be pushing an opponent over backwards, so larger, heavier lizards have the advantage. Such contests, though spectacular, are largely ritualised and seldom result in any serious damage to the participants.

SPOTTED TREE MONITOR

The Spotted Tree Monitor (*Varanus scalaris,* above) is a common arboreal monitor across much of tropical Australia. There is great variation in appearance between the regional populations; the rainforest dwellers of northern Queensland appear very different to those from the Kimberley region of Western Australia. It is likely that the Spotted Tree Monitor, as currently recognised, is actually a species complex — meaning it will eventually be split up into several species. It perches with its head lifted, facing the ground on a tree trunk and descends to seize passing insects and small lizards. When approached, it quickly climbs to the canopy and disappears into a hollow limb.

STEVE PARISH

A WIDESPREAD SPEEDSTER

The Sand Monitor (*Varanus gouldii*, above) is Australia's most common and widespread monitor. It is also known as the Racehorse Goanna, because it can run at high speed over flat terrain. Sand Monitors live in burrows in sandy soil, often beneath logs or at the base of spinifex grass. They forage widely for long periods of the morning and afternoon, searching for almost any animal able to be subdued and swallowed.

TREE-CLIMBING GOANNA

The Lace Monitor (*Varanus varius*) is the most familiar tree-climbing goanna of eastern Australia. It is equally at home in the rainforests of the coast or in the dry woodlands of western New South Wales. At 2 m in length, it is Australia's second-largest lizard and is an opportunistic feeder. Lace Monitors will raid birds' nests in the treetops for hatchlings and eggs, take fish and crayfish from drying creeks, or feed on road-killed animals, swallowing small ones whole and tearing away pieces of flesh and entrails from larger animals. Unlike some other species, it has lived alongside Cane Toads in eastern Australia for the past 70 years and does not attempt to eat them. It spends most of the day foraging on the ground, but quickly climbs a tall tree when threatened.

A SHY GIANT

The Perentie (below) inhabits arid, sandy environments from central Australia to the coast of Western Australia, and at 2.4 m, is Australia's largest lizard. Despite its size, it is timid and is not often seen. It is usually very quick to retreat, but an adult may stand its ground when approached and raise its body, extend its throat and hiss loudly in warning. At close quarters it lashes out with the tail, and will readily bite if provoked.

Above, top to bottom: Adult Lace Monitor. This broad-banded form occurs in dryer parts of the Lace Monitor's range; Juvenile Lace Monitor.

the FACTS!

ALL MONITORS LAY EGGS, generally in shallow burrows in the soil. At least two species, the Lace Monitor and the Heath Monitor, lay their eggs in active termite mounds. The termites quickly repair the damaged nest and the eggs are left to incubate in a secure, temperature and humidity controlled environment.

SOME OBSERVATIONS have led to suggestions that a female Heath Monitor (*Varanus rosenbergi*) returns to the termite nest where she laid her eggs, to liberate the young as they are hatching. But it is more likely that a female (perhaps the mother), digging into a nest to lay eggs, releases the hatchlings of a previous season by chance.

AUSTRALIA'S LARGEST monitor, the Perentie (bottom) shares much of its range, with the world's smallest monitor, the Short-tailed Monitor (*Varanus brevicauda*), which is fully grown at 20 cm.

THE MEGAFAUNA LIZARD *Megalania prisca*, was twice as big as a Komodo Dragon. Fossil evidence shows that it grew to over 7 m long and was capable of preying on animals many times its size. It is also known as the "Great Ripper" Lizard and was probably encountered by Aborigines when they first arrived in Australia approximately 60,000 years ago.

IN 2006, a Komodo Dragon named Flora at Chester Zoo, UK, produced a clutch of eggs without ever having been near a male. Researchers at the University of Liverpool used genetic tests to find that Flora had reproduced by parthenogenesis (without the involvement of a male). In the same year, a Komodo Dragon at London Zoo also had a "virgin birth".

KEN STEPNELL

Skinks
— worldwide distribution

Order: Squamata   **Suborder:** Sauria
Family: Scincidae

Skinks make up the most diverse and widespread lizard family on Earth and are especially successful in Australia, extending to all corners of the continent.

JUST ABOUT ANY HABITAT is skink territory, from Pedra Branca Islet, a rocky outcrop 26 km south-east of Tasmania, to the Torres Strait Islands off the tip of Cape York. They are most diverse in arid Australia, although some are equipped to handle colder temperatures. Australia's largest skink genus *Ctenotus*, which comprises the striped skinks (also known as "comb-eared" skinks) has 95 members, the majority of which occur in arid Australia.

Above: Docile Blotched Blue-tongues (*Tiliqua nigrolutea*) are often kept as pets.

the FACTS!

SKINKS ARE EXTREMELY successful lizards. Australia has more than 300 species — 60% of Australia's total lizard fauna.

THE VULNERABLE Pedra Branca Skink (*Nivoescincus palfreymani*) is confined to a rocky islet off the southern coast of Tasmania and is only active when the temperature rises above 15°C. It supplements its diet of insects with scraps of fish left over from seabird colonies.

SKINKS ARE the most cold-tolerant Australian lizards. With one exception, the Mountain Dragon (*Rankinia diemensis*), all Tasmanian lizards are skinks.

THE DEPRESSED SPINY SKINK (*Egernia depressa,* below) uses its short tail, covered with spiny bristles, as traction, wedging its spiky body into tight rock crevices to avoid predators.

THE TYPICAL SKINK

A typical skink is small and brown, with shiny overlapping scales, a tapering tail slightly longer than its body and small but functional limbs, each with five toes and claws. A skink's tightly fitting scales contain small plates of bone, making them firm to the touch and encasing the lizard in what looks and feels like shiny armour. The scales on top of its head are large and set out in a symmetrical pattern.

The Delicate Skink (*Lampropholis delicata*), a common resident of suburban gardens in eastern Australia, is a good example of a typical skink; however not all skinks fit this general description and there is much variation within the family. Some skinks have even adapted to a burrowing lifestyle by losing their limbs, either partially or wholly. Some burrowing skinks have long, slender bodies and very small, degenerate limbs. Others, like the Limbless Snake-tooth Skink (*Coeranoscincus frontalis*), from north Queensland rainforests, have no external trace of limbs.

SKINK LIFESTYLES

Most skinks are terrestrial and dig burrows in the soil, usually hidden among low vegetation or beneath rocks or logs. Others simply shelter beneath rocks, fallen bark or logs lying on the ground. In central Australia, striped skinks (*Ctenotus* spp.) prefer burrows at the base of spiky spinifex grass clumps. In the north-eastern rainforest, the Major Skink (*Egernia frerei*) lives in a burrow beneath moss-covered logs. Some skinks use rock crevices for shelter and many of these, like the Cunningham's Skink (*Egernia cunninghami*), have spiky scales. When a Cunningham's Skink inflates its spiny body in a tight rock crevice, it becomes impossible for a predator to extract the

Above: Cunningham's Skink (*Egernia cunninghami*)

lizard. Some skinks are arboreal, dwelling under loose bark or in tree hollows. Climbing skinks often have relatively long limbs and a flattened dorsal (back) surface, enabling them to squeeze beneath bark, or into a tight crevice.

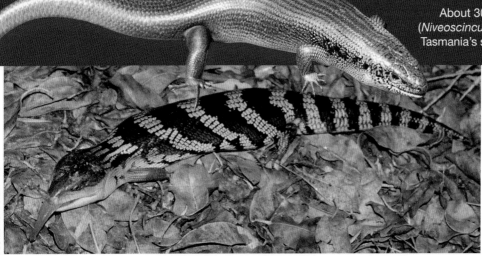

Below: The rare Obiri Rock Skink (*Bellatorias obiri*) is found only in Arnhem Land.

ABOVE & RIGHT: STEVE PARISH

Above: Blue-tongue lizards regularly poke out their bright blue tongues to "taste" their surroundings. Items of food are also investigated with the tongue prior to being eaten.

BACKYARD SUNBATHERS

Most skinks are diurnal and can be seen basking in the sun by day; however some are nocturnal or crepuscular (active during late afternoon or early morning). Temperature of the region usually determines whether skinks move about and forage by day or at night.

SUBURBAN SKINKS

Some small skinks, such as the Garden Skink (*Lampropholis guichenoti*), are more common in suburban yards and gardens than in nearby native bushland. The Fence Skink (*Cryptoblepharus pulcher*) is a tree-dwelling species that has successfully colonised the suburbs of eastern Australia's largest cities, where it is a common sight scampering across paling fences. It is an agile skink and in its natural arboreal habitat, makes short jumps from one branch to another.

The Eastern Blue-tongue (*Tiliqua scincoides scincoides*) adapts well to life in an overgrown suburban garden and is commonly encountered in built-up areas of Brisbane and Sydney. Shinglebacks (*Tiliqua rugosa*) are frequent visitors to the suburbs of Perth. A few skinks, such as the Golden Water Skink (*Eulamprus quoyii*), prefer a waterfront habitat and enter the water without hesitation when chased by a predator. Golden Water Skinks also thrive in city suburbs where they commonly inhabit concrete stormwater drains.

SNAKE COPY-CATS

The Centralian Blue-tongue (*Tiliqua multifasciata*) opens its mouth widely and flashes its bright blue tongue in warning when threatened. At the same time, it inflates its body in an effort to appear larger than it is and tucks its small legs in close, while angling its widest side towards an intruder. It is likely that the threatening behaviour of the Centralian Blue-tongue mimics the dangerously venomous Desert Death Adder (*Acanthophis pyrrhus*). Both reptiles share a similar distribution in arid Australia and both have short, robust bodies, with broad heads and a short tail. They are also similarly patterned with reddish-orange crossbands. Also, both the Desert Death Adder and the Centralian Blue-tongue flatten their bodies when feeling threatened. Of course, the Centralian Blue-tongue has legs, but they are a different colour to the body and, when tucked in close, are not immediately noticeable.

It is also likely that the Eastern Blue-tongue mimics the Common Death Adder (*Acanthophis antarcticus*) with its defensive display.

the FACTS!

AUSTRALIA'S LARGEST SKINK is the Land Mullet (*Bellatorias major*, above), so named because its shiny scales resemble those of the fish. It grows to 60 cm long, but most skinks are a lot smaller. One of the smallest skinks is the Top End Dwarf Skink (*Menetia alanae*) fully grown at just 7 cm.

REPTILE TICKS often attach themselves to blue-tongue lizards, particularly in the ear canal where they cannot be dislodged. Blue-tongue lizards are also subject to parasitic nematode worms in their intestines.

IN 2006, a man at Wiseman's Ferry in Sydney saved what he believed to be a blue-tongue lizard from the claws of a feral cat, only to be bitten five times by a very venomous (and ungrateful) Common Death Adder — the world's ninth deadliest snake.

Above: Apart from its often obscured legs and black facial stripe, the Centralian Blue-tongue closely resembles the dangerous Desert Death Adder in colouring.

About 500 Endangered Pygmy Blue-tongues (*Tiliqua adelaidensis*, right) are known to survive in small pockets of native grassland near the town of Burra, South Australia.

Above: The Shingleback protrudes its blue tongue and hisses to deter predators.

BACK FROM THE BRINK

The Pygmy Blue-tongue (*Tiliqua adelaidensis*) is a small, primitive blue-tongue that was thought to be extinct until it was rediscovered in 1992 after vanishing for more than three decades. It had not been sighted for 33 years when a herpetologist found one in the stomach of a road-killed Eastern Brown Snake (*Pseudonaja textilis*). Small remnant populations of the Pygmy Blue-tongue occur near the town of Burra in South Australia, and it is listed on the IUCN Red List of Threatened Species.

the FACTS!

IN MOST PARTS of the world, skinks are relatively small lizards, but in Australia many species are large and robust.

SOME SKINKS (including all of our large skinks) give birth to live young, and are the only Australian lizards to do so.

IN COLD WEATHER, blue-tongue lizards remain buried and inactive in shelter under rocks or logs. When active they use basking to keep their body temperature at 30–35°C.

WHEN A SHINGLEBACK'S CLUTCH consists of a single juvenile, it weighs an astonishing 35% of the mother's body weight at birth.

THE SLOW-MOVING Shingleback is an extremely long-lived lizard, with a life span of up to 50 years.

ENGLISH EXPLORER William Dampier, who first spotted the Shingleback in 1699, believed that the lizard had a "Head at each End". He also wrote, "I never did see such ugly creatures anywhere but here".

WHICH END IS WHICH?

The Shingleback (*Tiliqua rugosa*) is a large, robust skink with scales that resemble the overlapping seed casings of a pine cone. Its short, blunt tail is almost as wide as its head, so you could initially be left wondering which end is which. Appearing to have two heads is a defensive strategy that tricks predators into attacking the "expendable" tail end of a lizard, rather than the head, which could cause death. A Shingleback is too slow to run down live prey; instead it relies largely on a vegetarian diet and the tail is used to store fat. During good seasons, the tail becomes fatter, storing up energy reserves for lean times. Because it is unable to outrun a predator, a Shingleback will stand fast and throw open its large mouth to display its dark blue tongue when threatened. Should it have the opportunity to latch on to its tormentor with its powerful jaws, it delivers a painful, crushing bite.

It was long assumed that all reptiles were polygamous (mating with multiple, or any available partner), until recent studies shed light on the complex social life of the Shingleback. These lizards mate for life, but come together only during spring, when they seek out their partner of previous seasons. They find their partner again by following their mate's unique scent trail. For the duration of the mating season, about 6–8 weeks, they remain together in a monogamous relationship, parting again soon afterwards. A female Shingleback gives birth to two, or occasionally one or three, large young. It is thought that producing a small number of large young is a strategy to give the young a head start in times of drought.

Shinglebacks are very familiar lizards in southern Australia and have a variety of common names, including Pine Cone Lizard, Two-headed Lizard, Sleepy Lizard, Boggi, Stumpy-tailed Lizard and Bobtail.

Above: A Shingleback adopts its typical defensive posture, displaying its triangular, blue-violet tongue.

STEVE PARISH

Above: The male Jewel Rainbow Skink (rear) has iridescent speckling on the sides and almost appears to be a different species from the female (front).

Above: Male Jewel Rainbow Skinks have a bright orange stripe on their lower sides.

ALL THE COLOURS OF THE RAINBOW

It can be extremely difficult to tell the sex of a skink, because there is no obvious difference between males and females of most species; rainbow skinks in the genus *Carlia* are the exception. Most male rainbow skinks develop bright colours in the breeding season, probably to advertise their presence to rival males. The Slender Rainbow Skink (*Carlia gracilis*) is a common skink in well-watered gardens of suburban Darwin. It is normally a plain greyish brown in colour, but the male develops a blue-green flush on the head and a red stripe on its upper flanks during the breeding season. The spectacular colouring of a male Jewel Rainbow Skink (*Carlia jarnoldae*) includes a greenish head, blue spots on the upper flanks and an orange stripe below.

Rainbow skinks have a habit of lifting their tail and wriggling it about, seemingly to draw attention to themselves. Why they do this is not fully understood, but it appears to be a form of social communication, because the movements intensify when an individual encounters another skink in the leaf litter. It is also suggested that tail wriggling might be designed to draw the attention of a predator to its dispensable tail.

the FACTS!

MANY OF THE SMALLER SKINK species look very similar and are often difficult to identify without detailed, microscopic examination of their scalation.

THE DEGENERATE LIMBS of skinks such as the Southern Slider (*Lerista labialis*, below) differ from those of the legless lizards. The remnant hindlimbs of legless lizards are flap-like and are generally held flush against the sides, whereas those of skinks stick out from the body and, though very small, are usually more noticeable.

THE SOUTHERN SLIDER has no forelimbs, only remnant hindlimbs with two digits on each.

LEGLESS SKINKS

Many small skinks have a hidden lifestyle, burrowing in loose soil, sand or leaf litter. These burrowing skinks tend to have elongated bodies and may be missing part or all of their toes and limbs. Within the large genus *Lerista*, known as "sliders", species illustrate a complete range of gradual limb degeneration. Some slider species have four limbs, each with five toes, but other species show various degrees of toe and limb reduction and a few are entirely limbless. The varying degrees of modification match a particular species' burrowing habits. Species that spend most of their time above ground have well-developed limbs, while those that rarely come to the surface do not need to walk, so have reduced or absent limbs.

Above, top to bottom: It is easy to overlook the limbs of the Three-toed Skink (*Saiphos equalis*); The Limbless Snake-tooth Skink (*Coeranoscincus frontalis*).

51

KEN STEPNELL

STEVE PARISH

Above: Western Blue-tongue
(*Tiliqua occidentalis*)

Above right: Eastern Blue-tongues
(*Tiliqua scincoides scincoides*)

the FACTS!

SKINKS, LIKE ALL LIZARDS, do not have to eat every day. They eat when they have the need, or when food is available to them.

PESTICIDES USED to kill insects in the garden can also kill skinks, which ingest the pesticide when they eat affected insects.

THE FENCE SKINK (*Cryptoblepharus pulcher*) robs ant columns, ambushing the worker ants and relieving them of their load of ant larvae or dead insects.

MANY SKINKS SPONTANEOUSLY drop their tails when seized.

SNAKE SKINKS in the genus *Ophioscincus* are made up of three species, all of which have only miniscule stump-like limbs or are missing limbs altogether. Queensland is home to all three species, including the Short-limbed Snake Skink (*Ophioscincus truncatus*, below, also found in New South Wales), the Cooloola Snake Skink (*Ophioscincus cooloolensis*) and the Orange-bellied Snake Skink (*Ophioscincus ophioscincus*).

SKINK SNACKS

Insects are the primary food source for most small skinks, and the abundance of termites in arid and northern Australia has probably led to the diversity of small to medium-sized skinks in those regions. Larger skinks also eat insects but add other invertebrates such as worms and snails, as well as fruit, flowers and fungi to their diet. Burrowing, rainforest-dwelling skinks in the genus *Coeranoscincus* have recurved teeth that are probably specialised for a diet of earthworms. The strongly clawed Pink-tongued Skink (*Cyclodomorphus gerrardii*, above right) inhabits humid forests in eastern Australia, where its long, somewhat prehensile, tail helps it manoeuvre in the treetops. It dines on snails, using rounded teeth at the back of its mouth to break into snail shells. Most skinks are carnivorous and some will also prey on others within the Scincidae family. Most of the largest skinks, such as blue-tongue lizards and the Land Mullet, prefer to dine on vegetation and fungi.

SWIMMING THROUGH THE SAND

Sand swimmers in the genus *Eremiascincus* are named for their habit of "swimming" beneath the surface of loose sand. Two species range throughout Australia's sandy desert regions and both of them have four, conspicuous limbs. A sand swimmer's scales are glossy with low, rounded keels that are ideally arranged to allow these lizards to move in loose sand. Both the Narrow-banded Sand Swimmer (*Eremiascincus fasciolatus,* below) and the Broad-banded Sand Swimmer (*Eremiascincus richardsonii*) push themselves into sandy soil to escape predators or to shelter from the daytime heat. They also erupt from partially submerged positions in the sand to ambush passing insects or smaller lizards.

Below: Spiny-tailed Skinks (*Egernia stokesii*)

NEST SHARING

Some small skinks choose to lay their eggs in a communal nesting site, however scientists do not understand why the skinks choose to lay their eggs together, when it appears there are many equally suitable sites nearby.

EGG-LAYING & LIVE-BEARING

In typical reptile fashion, most skinks lay eggs, but among the family are the only Australian lizards to bear their young alive. Most live-bearers inhabit cooler regions, where giving birth to live young provides the distinct advantage of being able to protect developing embryos from the weather. A live-bearing skink can move from a cool location to a warmer one, or bask, but once eggs are laid, they are vulnerable to the elements. Live-bearing tropical species may have developed this ability in cooler periods of their evolutionary past, or it was developed in colder regions and live-bearing skinks later spread to the tropics.

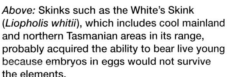

Above: Skinks such as the White's Skink (*Liopholis whitii*), which includes cool mainland and northern Tasmanian areas in its range, probably acquired the ability to bear live young because embryos in eggs would not survive the elements.

Below: A communal nesting site of the Delicate Skink (*Lampropholis delicata*) may contain as many as 250 eggs of this species in one location.

the FACTS!

MOST REPTILES are solitary, only coming together to mate, but some skinks (notably members of the genus *Egernia*) prefer instead to live in a community.

MATING FOR LARGER SKINK species can be quite rough and female blue-tongue lizards often have scrape and bite marks on their skin from the male's teeth.

ROCK-DWELLING Spiny-tailed Skinks (*Egernia stokesii*) live in stable social groups, numbering four or five individuals, or occasionally up to fifteen. These groups are usually made up of a male, female and different sized offspring of previous seasons. Juvenile Spiny-tailed Skinks may remain within their family group for five years until they reach maturity and disperse.

SPINY-TAILED SKINKS recognise other members of their family group by their scent.

SKINK SPECIES that do not give birth to live young, such as Strauch's Striped Skink (*Ctenotus strauchii*, below) usually lay their eggs under leaf litter, logs or in shallow holes in the soil. The eggs are oval-shaped, white and rubbery and are permeable, absorbing moisture from the damp soil.

Above: Tiger Snake
(*Notechis scutatus*)

Snakes
— slender magnificence

Order: Squamata
Suborder: Serpentes
Families: Typhlopidae, Pythonidae, Acrochordidae, Colubridae, Homalopsidae & Elapidae

Snakes are most simply described as long, slender reptiles without any legs; however, some lizards also fit this description. The evolutionary history of snakes is not fully understood and scientists have different opinions about their origin. Because of their fragile skeletons, they do not turn up in the fossil record very often.

the FACTS!

AUSTRALIAN SNAKES RANGE in size from the tiny Flowerpot Snake (*Ramphotyphlops braminus*), fully grown at 17 cm, to the Scrub Python (*Morelia kinghorni*), which sometimes reaches a length of 8 m.

OF SOME 3000 SPECIES of snakes worldwide, 188 are recorded in Australia.

AUSTRALIA'S SNAKES can be divided into six major snake families: blind snakes, pythons, file snakes, colubrid snakes, water snakes and venomous elapid snakes.

SNAKES HAVE up to 400 individual vertebrae and a single functional lung that can measure over two-thirds of their body length. The second lung is absent or much smaller and of little use.

SNAKE OR LIZARD?
- Snakes have no limbs, most lizards do.
- Snakes have no ears, most lizards do.
- Snakes have no eyelids, most lizards do.
- Snakes have a forked tongue, most lizards (with the exception of monitors) don't.

SNAKE EVOLUTION

Snakes are thought to have evolved from lizards, their nearest relatives, around 130 million years ago. The most widely accepted theory is that they evolved from a burrowing, monitor-like ancestor. Monitors have a similar skull structure to snakes and, like snakes, have forked tongues. It has been suggested that ancestral snakes lost their limbs after pursuing a burrowing lifestyle and then later re-emerged and spread to fill available environments above the ground. A rare lizard, the burrowing, semi-aquatic Earless Monitor (*Lanthanotus borneensis*) of Borneo, gives scientists some indication of how snake ancestors might have looked. Other living lizard families have members that show partial or complete limb loss as a result of a burrowing lifestyle, which also provides an indication of what might have happened to the limbs of ancestral snakes. Some primitive, living snakes, such as pythons and blind snakes, have traces of hindlimb or pelvic structures, which suggests they evolved from an ancestor that had limbs. Some scientists believe that snakes evolved from extinct, sea dwelling mosasaurs; but in 2006, the discovery of a fossilised 90-million-year-old snake with "hips", named *Najash rionegrina*, in Argentina cast doubt on the theory.

Above: The recurved teeth of a python are used to grip prey and are unsuitable for cutting or tearing.

Below: The Marsh Snake (*Hemiaspis signata*) is a live-bearing snake that gives birth to up to sixteen offspring. It inhabits the edges of waterways and swamps along Australia's eastern coast.

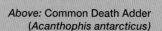

Above: Common Death Adder
(*Acanthophis antarcticus*)

SLITHERING ALONG

People are fascinated by the way that snakes are able to move purposefully and gracefully without the aid of limbs. Most terrestrial snakes do this by "lateral undulation" — using waves of muscle contractions to move the forebody from side to side, creating a series of sideways loops in the snake's body. The snake's belly scales, find traction on irregularities on the ground's surface, propelling the body forward. For this reason, snakes have difficulty moving across very smooth surfaces, but their lateral undulation works very well in water and most are excellent swimmers. Aquatic snakes have adaptations such as laterally flattened bodies, or, in the case of marine snakes, paddle-like tails that enable them to move beneath the water with speed and dexterity. Some large snakes move forward in a straight line using muscles attached to their belly scales in a process called "rectilinear motion". Others use a "sidewinding motion", where the body is lifted from the ground in a series of loops and the snake is propelled diagonally in relation to the direction it faces. Sidewinding is ideal on smooth surfaces or in loose sand. Another method is "concertina motion", where the rear of the body is simply pulled forward in a series of lateral loops and the front of the body then thrust forward.

EXTRAORDINARY SENSES

Snakes have no external ears, but they are able to hear very low frequency sounds using their inner ears. They are also alerted to approaching prey or predators by picking up vibrations from the ground through the scales on the head and belly. In addition to this, snakes "smell their way" by constantly flicking the tongue in and out of the mouths. The tongue picks up airborne scent particles and transfers them to a sensory organ, called Jacobson's organ, on the roof of the mouth — in this way a snake is "tasting" its surroundings. Snakes have no eyelids, instead their eyes are covered with a transparent scale. Many snakes have excellent eyesight.

Below: A Tiger Snake's forked tongue transmits smell signals to its Jacobson's organ.

Above: Prey is engulfed by the snake's flexible jaws and digested in the stomach.

SWALLOWED ALIVE!

Snakes capture live prey and devour it whole, sometimes while it is still alive. Their needle-like, backwards-curving teeth are designed to grip prey, but not to cut or chew. Because snakes have highly elastic skin and loosely attached bones in the jaw and skull, they are able to swallow animals much larger than themselves. Some pythons are able to swallow animals up to five times the diameter of their own neck! The sides of a snake's lower jaw are attached at the front with an elastic ligament, allowing them to spread widely apart. This enables the snake to inch each side of the jaw forward independently, virtually "walking" its skull over its prey.

the FACTS!

SNAKES TRAVELLING over uneven terrain might give the impression they are moving at considerable speed, but in reality, the fastest snake is no match for the brisk walking pace of a human.

ARBOREAL SNAKES, such as the Brown Tree Snake (*Boiga irregularis*, below) slither along branches or wind their strong tails around tree trunks to enable them to strike.

SNAKES HAVE an extendable trachea (windpipe). While swallowing, the tracheal opening is extended past its prey like a straw, enabling the snake to breathe and swallow its bulky meal at the same time.

SOME SNAKES have developed venom to help them secure their prey. This very serious health risk, added to the fact that all snakes are protected, means that people should never attempt to kill or interfere with snakes.

Blind snakes
— earthworm impersonators

Order: Squamata   **Suborder:** Serpentes
Family: Typhlopidae

Above: A Prong-snouted Blind Snake (*Ramphotyphlops bituberculatus*) in a knotted defensive posture.

the FACTS!

ANT PUPAE, larvae and occasionally adult ants, ant eggs and termites are on the menu for blind snakes, which are Australia's only insectivorous snakes.

THE TINY FLOWERPOT SNAKE (*Ramphotyphlops braminus,* right) is the only snake in the world known to reproduce parthenogenetically. This means that all Flowerpot Snakes are female and all offspring are a direct clone of their mother.

AUSTRALIA HAS only one genus of blind snake, the genus *Ramphotyphlops,* within which there are presently 43 recognised Australian species.

LITTLE IS KNOWN about the reproduction of most species of blind snake, but scientists assume all are egg layers. One species, the Southern Blind Snake (*Ramphotyphlops australis*), is known to lay about five eggs in midsummer, with the eggs ranging in size from 2–2.5 cm.

STUDIES OF SPECIMENS of blind snakes held in museums throughout Australia showed that some individuals had recently eaten as many as 1 400 prey items!

RESEARCHERS HAVE BEGUN to shed some light on the secret lives of blind snakes. They are now known to recognise and react to the scent trails of foraging ants and follow the trails to locate nests.

At a glance, a blind snake could easily be mistaken for a large earthworm, and because they share similar burrowing habits, we consequently know little about them. Although they stay mainly underground, blind snakes are occasionally active on the surface, particularly on warm humid nights.

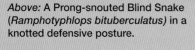

A UNIQUE & PRIMITIVE FAMILY

Blind snakes are a primitive family and have remnants of pelvic bones, reminding us that they evolved from a limbed ancestor. There are around 150 species worldwide, but they are so unlike all other snakes that some people have questioned whether they are snakes at all.

MODIFIED FOR A SUBTERRANEAN LIFESTYLE

Blind snakes vary from species to species, from slender to robust, but all are more or less long and cylindrical along the entire length of the body from the blunt, rounded snout to the tail. The tail ends with a short spine, which is pushed against the soil to help the blind snake move through tight spaces within ant nests. A blind snake's highly polished scales also help it move through the soil. Another modification for a subterranean lifestyle is a blind snake's rudimentary eyes, which simply appear as small black spots beneath the head shields. A blind snake's eyes can distinguish light from dark, but probably not much else, as good eyesight is irrelevant for a life lived burrowing beneath the ground. Ant larvae, a blind snake's main food source, is taken into the small, curved, shark-like mouth that is positioned well back from the snout.

Below: A blind snake's smooth, shiny scales are almost uniform in size, and its pinkish skin and blunt snout make it resemble a worm.

IAN MORRIS

MICHAEL CERMAK

Above: A soldier ant attacking a marauding blind snake.

HARMLESS TO HUMANS, THE SCOURGE OF ANTS

Blind snakes are totally harmless and are unable to bite humans. They are also non-venomous. The best defence they can muster is to push their tail spine meekly against the skin or to emit a foul-smelling liquid from their anal glands, which might also be used to repel the attacks of ants, which blind snakes encounter when they enter ants' nests seeking food.

Ants are the favoured food of blind snakes, which feed on ant pupae and larvae and occasionally adult ants, ant eggs and termites. Studies on collected specimens show that their stomachs often contain numerous prey, usually of a single species, suggesting that blind snakes enter ant nests and remain there, feeding within them. They may even live in ant nests. Research on blind snakes in other countries has revealed that they are rapid feeders, taking in up to 80 ant pupae each minute. Most ants, particularly soldier ants, are fiercely protective of their nests, and scientists don't yet understand how blind snakes are able to fend off the attacking ants. It may be that the ants' mandibles cannot grip the smooth, firm surface of the snake's cylindrical body. Blind snakes feed on ant species in relation to their size. Small blind snakes feed on small species and large blind snakes on large ant species, so the diameter of the blind snake's body is probably too large for the ants' mandibles to deliver a pinching bite.

RARELY ENCOUNTERED

Australia has 43 recognised species of blind snakes, but six are represented in Australian museums by only a single specimen and some have never been photographed in life. In 1998, an unknown and very unusual blind snake was brought to the surface by a drilling rig on remote Barrow Island, off the coast of Western Australia. Its lack of pigmentation suggests that it does not naturally venture to the surface. The Slender Blind Snake is a long, pale, slender blind snake and appropriately, has been bestowed with a long, slender scientific name, *Ramphotyphlops longissimus*. In Australia, there are also probably many new species of blind snake still awaiting discovery. Consider that Australia's third-largest snake, the Oenpelli Python (*Morelia oenpelliensis*)— a 4.5 m python that has a habit of sitting out in the sun — was unknown to science until 1977 and you can imagine how easy it would be for a 20 cm, worm-like, subterranean blind snake to go undetected. Blind snakes are a little studied family — even some herpetologists find it difficult to get excited about them, and many are difficult to identify without a detailed microscopic examination of their scales.

Above: The stomach of one Robust Blind Snake (*Ramphotyphlops ligatus*) contained 206 prey animals, mostly ant pupae and larvae. This Robust Blind Snake is about to shed its skin.

Below: Wied's Blind Snake (*Ramphotyphlops wiedii*) usually only comes to the surface after dark.

Below: The pinkish to mauve South-eastern Blind Snake (*Ramphotyphlops nigrescens*) is common around Sydney.

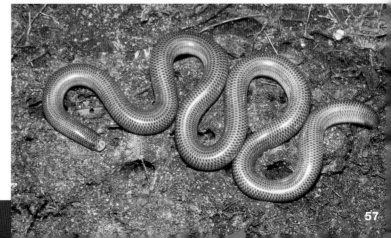

Pythons
— masses of muscle

Order: Squamata
Suborder: Serpentes **Family:** Pythonidae

The family Pythonidae includes the world's largest snakes, all of which are non-venomous. In Australia, pythons are familiar snakes to many people because they frequently curl themselves up in the rafters of house or shed roofs, where they feed on birds and rodents.

KEN STEPNELL

Above: An Eastern Carpet Python (*Morelia mcdowelli*) makes short work of a parrot.

SNAKES WITH LEGS?

Herpetologists know that pythons are very primitive snakes because they retain a pelvis and remnant hindlimbs, which are visible only as a tiny spur on either side of the snake's anal (cloacal) vent. Males have slightly larger spurs than females and use them to stimulate females by stroking their flanks during courtship.

PYTHONS ARE POWERFUL, well-muscled snakes that envelop their prey in their tight body coils and constrict it until it can no longer breathe and dies of suffocation (asphyxiation). Even animals that are much larger than the python itself can be despatched in this manner and are then swallowed whole. Pythons are able to swallow such large prey items because of their loosely joined jaw bones and the high elasticity of their skin. Once a python's sometimes astonishing feat is accomplished, the snake becomes inactive until its meal is digested. As a result, slow-moving pythons with grossly distended stomachs are sometimes discovered caught in chicken coops.

IAN MORRIS

Above, top to bottom: A glutted Water Python cannot escape a chicken coop; The Black-headed Python has no heat-sensitive labial pits and feeds largely on reptiles.

STEALTH & PATIENCE

Birds, reptiles and especially small mammals are the most common prey for pythons, which sometimes actively seek out prey, but are more usually ambush predators. Most pythons adopt a position near an area or pathway where mammals are likely to pass by. Eastern Carpet Pythons (*Morelia spilota mcdowelli*), are particularly patient, and have been observed waiting in the same position night after night, biding their time for an opportunity to seize a passing rodent. Such stealthy tactics mean that most pythons are nocturnal, however all species will also bask during the day when conditions are favourable, especially while digesting their prey. After swallowing a large meal, and weather permitting, a python might remain coiled and motionless in the open for a number of days.

the FACTS!

THE WORLD'S LARGEST SNAKE, the Reticulated Python (*Python reticulatus*) of south-east Asia, has been recorded at 10.1 m and, on rare occasions, has been known to swallow humans.

AUSTRALIA'S LARGEST SNAKE, the Scrub Python (*Morelia kinghorni*), is capable of subduing and swallowing a wallaby or small kangaroo.

A PYTHON'S JAWS are equipped with long, needle-sharp, recurved teeth, and a large snake can deliver a painful, but non-venomous, bite.

Right: Eastern Carpet Pythons vary greatly in appearance, and may bear stripes, blotches, bands, or a combination of these markings.

Conservation Watch

The distinctive south-western and eastern populations of the Woma are Endangered due to large-scale clearing of their habitat for agriculture.

Above: Womas have been observed to wriggle their tail tip to attract animals, which they then devour.

HEAT-SEEKING LIPS

To help them catch warm-blooded mammalian prey at night, most pythons have infra-red, heat receptive pits (known as labial pits) along the side of the jaw. The exceptions to this are the Woma (*Aspidites ramsayi*) and the Black-Headed Python (*Aspidites melanocephalus*), which both prefer cold-blooded reptilian prey.

A RARE REPTILE-EATER

The Woma occurs in sandy locations across much of arid Australia. It has some immunity to the venom of the snakes on which it feeds, including that of the highly venomous brown snakes and King Brown Snake (*Pseudechis australis*). The Woma attacks other reptiles living in holes in the ground and kills them using constriction.

Above: Heat-seeking pits can be seen on this Carpet Python's lower jaw. Studies on pythons in other parts of the world suggest these organs can pick up changes in temperature that are as small as 1/30th of a degree!

Above: Adult Green Tree Pythons are bright green.

Right: A yellow juvenile Green Tree Python.

GREEN & GOLD

Prehensile tails (adapted for gripping) and muscular bodies give pythons an advantage in the treetops and many are partly arboreal. Adult Green Tree Pythons (*Morelia viridis*) rarely leave the trees. They are widely distributed throughout New Guinea, but Australian individuals are confined to a few pockets of rainforest in northern Cape York Peninsula. By day, a Green Tree Python curls itself up into a tight symmetrical ball, resting on a branch with its head at the centre of its coils. By night, adults hunt for birds and small mammals within the rainforest, often high in the canopy. In contrast, juvenile Green Tree Pythons are mainly active by day, hunting small lizards near the ground in comparatively open areas at the edge of the rainforest. Feeding habits are not the only, or most significant, difference between adult and juveniles. Juvenile Green Tree Pythons are not green at all when they emerge from the egg — to date, all Australian juveniles recorded have been bright yellow. An abrupt transformation to the green adult colouration takes place after about a year. The variation in colour reflects the different environmental preferences. As a subadult snake reaches a size where it is possible to begin preying on birds and small mammals, it moves into the closed forest habitat and undergoes the colour change, which reduces its visibility to predators in its new environment.

the FACTS!

AUSTRALIA HAS THIRTEEN python species, approximately half of the world's 26 python species. They are most abundant and diverse in the tropical north.

THE EXTENT OF PYTHON diversity in Australia and New Guinea probably indicates that pythons evolved in this region.

THE GENUS *Aspidites,* which includes the Woma and the Black-headed Python, is endemic to Australia. Some scientists believe they may be the closest living relatives to the earliest pythons.

THE GREEN TREE PYTHON bears a striking resemblance to the Emerald Tree Boa (*Corallus caninus*) of South America, but they are not closely related. They are the same size, adults are similarly coloured, both change colour from juvenile to adult and both are arboreal, resting coiled in the branches by day. Together they are one of the most spectacular examples of convergent evolution, where animals independently develop similar characteristics to suit comparable ecosystems.

Above and right: Water Pythons feed mainly on rats and other small mammals.

STEVE PARISH

the FACTS!

THE WORLD'S SMALLEST PYTHON, the Pygmy Python (*Antaresia perthensis*) of Western Australia, is fully grown at 60 cm. It haunts tunnels and cavities of large termite mounds searching for the geckoes on which it feeds.

AUSTRALIA'S RAREST PYTHON, the Rough-scaled Python (*Morelia carinata*, below) was not known to science until 1975 and remained undescribed until 1981. It is known from just ten snakes captured in the wild and efforts to study it are made more difficult by the fact that it inhabits isolated rocky gorges in the northern Kimberley region of Western Australia. The Australian Reptile Park near Sydney, in conjunction with the Western Australian conservation department (CALM) now runs a captive breeding program for the species and, for the first time, successfully bred this snake in captivity in January 2001.

IAN MORRIS

OENPELLI PYTHONS are able to change their colour at night. By day they are brown on top, but at night they become pale grey.

Right: The Northern Territory Wildlife Park is hoping to start a volunteer breeding program for the Oenpelli Python.

IAN MORF

A DUSKY RAT'S NEMESIS

The brilliantly iridescent Water Python (*Liasis mackloti*) is semi-aquatic. In the Northern Territory dry season, it shelters during the day among dense reed beds in swamps or in cavities among the roots of paperbark trees. At night, it goes in search of the abundant Dusky Rat (*Rattus colletti*), which lives in deep soil cracks in the surrounding floodplain. During the wet season, when the floodplain is submerged, the rats migrate to higher ground and the Water Pythons must either follow or remain in the water and switch their diet to nesting waterbirds and their eggs, or occasional juvenile Freshwater Crocodiles (*Crocodylus johnstoni*).

AN EXCITING DISCOVERY

At about 4.5 m in length, the Oenpelli Python (*Morelia oenpelliensis*) is one of Australia's largest pythons, but incredibly, it was unknown to science until 1977. In that year, it was described by Graeme Gow, then curator of reptiles at the Northern Territory Museum, from a snake discovered by Brian Jukes, a schoolteacher and amateur herpetologist living at Oenpelli. That such a large and distinctive snake was overlooked for so long is testimony to the isolation of its habitat and the ruggedness of the remote terrain. The Oenpelli Python is restricted to rock formations of eastern Arnhem Land in the Northern Territory, where it shelters in deep crevices and caves. It can also be found in trees adjacent to the cliff face. Flying-foxes, possums and rock-wallabies are the major components of its diet.

STEVE PARISH

Conservation Watch

The Threatened Pilbara Olive Python (*Liasis olivaceus barroni*) is confined to the Pilbara region of WA. One aim of researchers is to minimise the number of these pythons killed on roads.

Above: The Olive Python (*Liasis olivaceus olivaceus*) is commonly seen around waterholes amid rocky areas in Australia's north.

A FARMER'S FRIEND

There are seven distinct subspecies within the Carpet and Diamond Python complex (*Morelia spilota*), found across much of Australia. They are the only pythons that live close to the large cities of south-eastern and south-western Australia, and so are Australia's most familiar pythons. In rural areas, these pythons are familiar residents in farm sheds and are often encouraged to remain because they help to reduce the population of rats and mice. The beautifully patterned Diamond Python (*Morelia spilota spilota*) of eastern New South Wales differs substantially in colour and pattern to its northern counterpart, the Eastern Carpet Python (*Morelia spilota mcdowelli*). However, where their ranges join in the northern rivers district of New South Wales, there is a hybrid zone where the population has various combinations of Diamond Python and Eastern Carpet Python pattern, showing just how closely related the two subspecies are.

Above: The Jungle Carpet Python (*Morelia spilota cheynei*) is one of the most colourful *spilota* subspecies.

the FACTS!

THE BLUFF DOWNS GIANT Python, known from fossil material unearthed at Bluff Downs, north of Charters Towers in Queensland, lived about four million years ago and has been estimated to be about 10 m long — larger than most modern snakes. Its closest living relative is the Olive Python (*Liasis olivaceous,* top).

FEMALE PYTHONS are able to raise their body temperature while coiled around their eggs by performing "shivering" muscular contractions.

DURING THE BREEDING SEASON, male Green Tree Pythons fight and captive specimens have been known to kill one another. Facing off, rearing up and attempting to force down an opponent means the largest, bulkiest contestant is usually the winner.

A PYTHON HOLDS the world record for longevity among snakes. A Ball Python (*Python regius*) acquired as a young adult by the Philadelphia Zoo in the USA, lived for more than 47 years.

EGG LAYERS

Female pythons make attentive parents and take care of their eggs — a feature rare among reptiles. All pythons are egg layers and eggs are often bonded together to form an egg mass. While the embryos develop inside the eggshell, the mother usually remains coiled about the eggs to incubate them at a suitable temperature and to deter predators. Once the young slit the parchment-like shell with their egg tooth, they disperse and are on their own.

Right: A juvenile Green Tree Python (*Morelia viridis*) emerging from its egg.

MICHAEL CERMAK

File snakes
— unlikely to win a beauty contest

the FACTS!

Order: Squamata **Suborder:** Serpentes
Family: Acrochordidae

THE LITTLE FILE SNAKE has a salt-expelling gland beneath the tongue, like those of marine snakes. From this it might be assumed they are related to marine snakes, but they are not. Both families have independently developed a salt excretion gland because they occupy the same ecological niche and are subject to the same environmental pressures.

FILE SNAKES HAVE a very low metabolic rate that enables them to stay underwater for at least an hour — probably longer in some circumstances! They are able to do this because they absorb some of their oxygen requirement from the water through the skin.

THE LITTLE FILE SNAKE occurs alongside dangerously venomous marine snakes in estuarine habitats, but can easily be distinguished by the absence of a paddle-shaped tail.

FILE SNAKES use "volmerolfaction" (tongue flicking to detect scent) to find prey.

ARAFURA FILE SNAKES often travel long distances to feed at night, but frequently return to the same resting area by day. This suggests that they have a "homing" ability that allows them to find their way to their daytime resting place.

CROCODILES ARE a major predator of file snakes, as are birds of prey such as the White-bellied Sea Eagle, which snatches them from the surface as they venture up to breathe.

Above: Arafura File Snakes are nocturnal reptiles that hunt at night.

Australia has two file snake species and both are unlike all other snakes in appearance. They receive their common name from the rough texture of their baggy skin, which resembles the surface of a file. A third species (Acrochordus javanicus) is found in South-East Asia, where these snakes are called "elephant trunk snakes" or "wart snakes".

SUPERBLY ADAPTED FOR AN AQUATIC LIFESTYLE

File snakes are aquatic, typically spending a long time under water and periodically making brief trips to the surface to breathe. A file snake's valvular nostrils and small eyes are positioned towards the front and top of its rather blunt head, so very little of the snake is visible at the surface when it takes a breath. They are excellent swimmers. Their bodies are moderately flattened sideways and this, together with their loose skin, enhances speed and manoeuvrability in the water. File snakes do not often choose to leave the water, but occasionally, if they become stranded by receding floodwaters or tides, they must cross a tidal flat or floodplain. On land, they move in a slow and awkward manner.

FILE SNAKE HABITATS

Files snakes live in tropical northern Australia, where the Arafura File Snake (*Acrochordus arafurae*) prefers freshwater habitats and the Little File Snake (*Acrochordus granulatus*) dwells in mangrove-lined estuaries and coastal regions.

Left: The Arafura File Snake is the largest Australian species, growing up to 2.1 m long.

Above: Aborigines of northern Australia consider Arafura File Snakes a great delicacy. They search under submerged logs and in holes in the river bank for these snakes, which, once caught, are roasted on hot coals and eaten.

Conservation Watch

File snakes are widespread and abundant in northern Australia and face no significant threat from human activity.

INFREQUENT BREEDERS

File snakes give birth to live young in the water, a trait they share with almost all aquatic snakes. The Arafura File Snake produces anywhere from 11–27 young, but reproduces only every few years. A female requires a number of good seasons to gain the condition needed to nourish developing young. Up to seven males may be seen attempting to mate with a single female in the wild, which indicates that pheromones help a male determine a sexually receptive female file snake.

FISH-EATERS

Fish make up most of the non-venomous file snake's diet. At night, the Arafura File Snake stalks sleeping fish in the shallow waters of a billabong, but also anchors itself among submerged roots by day and ambushes free-swimming fish, some of which may be quite large. Dead fish are also hungrily devoured.

The Little File Snake searches out small fish that are hiding in crevices on the sea bed, and its rasp-like skin helps it to grip its slippery prey. Once caught, the fish is restrained in the snake's body coils, in a similar manner to that used by pythons. Even while swallowing one meal, the Little File Snake may be catching another! It has been seen holding one fish with its tail while simultaneously swallowing another.

LITTLE FILE SNAKE

The Little File Snake grows to about 1 m and lives in shallow, mangrove-fringed estuaries or (occasionally) coastal freshwater swamps. They generally prefer shallow estuaries, but have been recorded 20 km from the shore in 20 m-deep water. Little File Snakes must periodically seek freshwater and reportedly drink rainwater, which briefly forms a layer on the surface of the sea. Unlike other snakes, which invert their old skin in the process of shedding it, the Little File Snake firstly loosens its skin from the body and then crawls out of it, usually without turning the skin inside out.

Above: The Little File Snake is also found in New Guinea, Indonesia, the Philippines and India.

ARAFURA FILE SNAKE

The secretive Arafura File Snake (left), though often present in large numbers in billabongs, is rarely observed. It hides by day beneath floating vegetation or among the roots of trees, particularly pandanus trees, in the shaded recesses of overhanging banks.

Above: The Keelback's distribution overlaps that of the venomous Rough-scaled Snake (*Tropidechis carinatus*), which is similar in size and appearance and also has keeled scales.

Colubrid snakes
— harmless land snakes

Order: Squamata **Suborder:** Serpentes
Family: Colubridae

Approximately 1 800 species and a near-global distribution, make Colubrid snakes by far the world's largest and most successful snake family. Surprisingly, Australia has just six species, all of which are relatively recent arrivals — so recent that none have yet diversified into local species.

ALL AUSTRALIAN COLUBRIDS also occur in other countries to the continent's north and colubrids probably first emigrated to Australia from New Guinea, across land bridges that existed during past periods of low sea levels. In Australia they are confined to the humid northern and eastern coasts and immediate hinterland. None occur in Australia's dry heartland, although given enough time (perhaps a few million years) they might evolve forms capable of moving into arid Australia. However, for the time being, Australia's dry regions remain the undisputed realm of the continent's most successful group of snakes, the front-fanged land snakes.

Above: The Common Tree Snake is a proficient climber, manoeuvring among foliage with speed and agility.

the FACTS!

THE EARLIEST KNOWN FOSSIL of a colubrid-like snake is from Thailand and dates to the late Eocene period of about 38.6–35.4 million years ago.

SOME HERPETOLOGISTS consider the family Colubridae to include as many as seven subfamilies, only four of which are represented in Australia. By this classification, these are the Colubrinae (terrestrial colubrids), the Natricinae (the sole member of which is the Keelback) and the Homalopsinae (aquatic colubrids). The accidental introduction of the Asian Wolf Snake (*Lycodon aulicus capucinus*) to Christmas Island has brought the subfamily Lycodontinae to Australian territory.

AFTER WWII, some Brown Tree Snakes accidentally found their way to the Pacific Island of Guam, where they caused the decline and extinction of some of the island's native fauna. To stop Brown Tree Snakes causing similar havoc on other Pacific islands, sniffer dogs have been trained to detect them in aeroplane cargo.

NOT SO NON-VENOMOUS

Traditionally, Australia's colubrid snakes have been regarded as non-venomous, or in the case of one species, the Brown Tree Snake (*Boiga irregularis*), rear-fanged and mildly venomous. However, researchers have now turned this notion upside down. It appears that many of these so-called non-venomous colubrid snakes do indeed have venom, but it is in very small quantities and they lack the sophisticated venom-delivery mechanism of other snakes, such as elapids and vipers, to deliver it effectively (at least to humans). It was long held that the glands now recognised as venom glands in colubrid snakes (Duvernoy's gland), were

little more than salivary glands, releasing a kind of toxic saliva to the base of the teeth at the rear of the upper jaw, mainly for lubricating prey or to aid digestion. However, they are now considered to be true (although primitive) venom glands, from which the more efficient venom glands of elapid snakes and vipers are thought to have evolved. What is apparent, however, is that Australian colubrid snakes do not pose a threat to humans, because there have been countless recorded bites and none have had any medical consequences. So it is still reasonable to consider them harmless, but perhaps not to the frogs and other small animals on which they feed.

IAN MORRIS

the FACTS!

REMARKABLY, in a similar fashion to some lizards, the Keelback is able to break off the tip of its tail if it is grasped but it does not regrow.

BROWN TREE SNAKES silently stalk dragon lizards while they sleep exposed on branches of trees and shrubs during mild weather.

ALTHOUGH VENOMOUS, the Brown Tree Snake is not dangerous to humans. Its fangs, or enlarged grooved teeth, are located towards the rear of the jaw. The venom is delivered by holding and repeatedly chewing its prey.

THE NORTHERN TREE SNAKE (*Dendrelaphis calligastra*) grows to around 1 m in length and is a very slender snake that dwells in monsoon forest and vine thickets in northern Queensland and the Torres Strait Islands.

THE SLATE-BROWN SNAKE (*Stegonotus parvu*s) is common in New Guinea but is rare and poorly studied in Australia where it is confined to the Torres Strait Islands.

WHEN A COMMON TREE SNAKE is threatened, it rears up to strike but rarely bites, preferring to inflate its body to show off the blue-coloured skin between its scales.

AN APPETITE FOR AMPHIBIANS

The Keelback (*Tropidonophis mairii,* above) derives its common name from its strongly keeled body scales. It lives at the water's edge and feeds almost exclusively on frogs. Amazingly, the Keelback also has a strong resistance to the toxin of the introduced Cane Toad (*Bufo marinus*) and is one of only a few native Australian animals able to feed on them without ill effects. It also eats the eggs and tadpoles of the Cane Toad, as well as small toadlets.

NOCTURNAL PREDATOR

The nocturnal Brown Tree Snake preys on lizards, small mammals, birds and occasionally frogs. There are two distinctive races in Australia, which have in the past been considered separate species. The north-western race (right) is handsomely marked with terracotta and cream bands and is often referred to as "night tiger". The eastern race, sometimes called "doll's eye" in reference to its large eyes, is brown, with indistinct blackish bands and a salmon undersurface.

IAN MORRIS

A COLOURFUL COLUBRID

The Common Tree Snake (*Dendrelaphis punctulata*, below) comes in a wide variety of colours, from golden yellow with a pale blue head and neck in the north-west, to olive green, brown, black or occasionally blue on the east coast. The variety of colours among Common Tree Snakes probably indicates that they are actively evolving.

REPTILIAN EGG-EATER

The Slatey-grey Snake (*Stegonotus cucullatus*) is glossy brownish grey to black in colour and lives on the ground beneath debris or in soil cracks. Reptile eggs feature largely in its diet, often those of the Keelback. It also eats frogs, small mammals, lizards and fish.

Above: The Bockadam has a broad head and can easily swallow whole fish, even ones that are quite large.

Water snakes
— aquatic ambushers

Order: Squamata **Suborder:** Serpentes
Family: Homalopsidae

Some herpetologists consider water snakes to be a subfamily of the Colubridae, called Homalopsinae, but others maintain that they live sufficiently different lifestyles to warrant their own family: Homalopsidae.

FOUR SPECIES OF WATER SNAKES occur in both saltwater and freshwater environments along the tropical northern coast of Australia and all are the sole representatives of their genus in Australia. All species also extend further to the north of Australia and one, the White-bellied Mangrove Snake (*Fordonia leucobalia*), ranges throughout south-east Asia, where it is known as the Crab-eating Snake. Three of the four species of Australian water snake live in salt or brackish waters, in estuaries and tidal reaches of rivers and creeks. They haunt the fringes of waterways and shun open water to avoid being eaten by large fish. Crocodiles and birds also prey on water snakes.

All of them have useful adaptations for their underwater lifestyles, including valvular nostrils that are positioned on the upper surface of the snout and close when the snake is submerged. Water snakes' tiny bulging eyes are also positioned upwards, enabling the snake to poke its head out of the water to see and breathe at the surface while the rest of its body remains underwater.

the FACTS!

WATER SNAKES are relatively small, stout snakes. The largest is fully grown at about 90 cm.

WATER SNAKES in the family Homalopsidae are mildly venomous and can be distinguished from dangerously venomous marine elapid snakes by their cylindrical, tapering tails. In contrast, dangerous sea snakes in the family Elapidae have distinctly paddle-shaped tails. However, to be on the safe side it is best not to handle any aquatic snakes you encounter.

FEW PEOPLE venture into tropical swamps or mangrove-lined estuaries at night, so most water snakes are rarely encountered.

IF A CRAB IS TOO LARGE to be swallowed whole by a White-bellied Mangrove Snake, the snake presses it against the mud with its body coil and the claws and legs are then broken off and swallowed one by one. The White-bellied Mangrove Snake is the only snake known to dismember its prey.

THE RARE Richardson's Mangrove Snake (*Myron richardsonii*) exists in tidal creeks and estuaries along Australia's north coast as well as in Indonesia and New Guinea.

WATER SNAKES have no need to leave the water to lay eggs, all species give birth to live young.

THE UNIQUE CRAB-EATING SNAKE

A population of White-bellied Mangrove Snakes (above) can include individual snakes of such a wide variety of colours and patterns that they almost defy description, and herpetologists do not understand why. In the past, some colour forms have wrongly been considered as separate species. Individuals may be spotted, variegated, striped or plain. It is an inhabitant of mangrove swamps, haunting channels, crab holes and the mounds of the Mud Lobster (*Thalassina anomala*) in the intertidal zone. It is most often encountered at night on exposed mudflats at low tide. It preys almost exclusively on crabs, but is also recorded feeding on Mud Lobsters and shrimps. The White-bellied Mangrove Snake, together with blind snakes, which feed on ant pupae, larvae and eggs, are the only Australian snakes known to prey on invertebrates.

Above: Bockadam

Above: White-bellied Mangrove Snake

AN ESTUARINE WATER SNAKE

The Bockadam (*Cerberus australis*) is fully aquatic, inhabiting saltwater or brackish, mangrove-lined creeks. Unlike the White-bellied Water Snake, it doesn't leave the water by choice. It feeds at night on small fish, which it corners in shallows at the water's edge. The Bockadam's keeled body scales help it negotiate the slippery, muddy terrain. In the Northern Territory, most Bockadams are grey in colour and well camouflaged against the mangrove mud of their habitat; however a small percentage are brick-red and highly visible. Why they are so coloured is a mystery.

FRESHWATER SPECIALISTS

Macleay's Water Snakes (*Enhydris polylepis,* below) are fully aquatic, found in freshwater reaches of rivers, creeks, billabongs and swamps in north Queensland and the Northern Territory. They frequent areas that have dense aquatic vegetation, because their method of attack is to anchor to vegetation, adopting a camouflaged position and then ambushing passing fish. In the Northern Territory, the Macleay's Water Snake ventures out onto flooded plains during the wet season to feed on sleeping fish in the shallows at night. It is capable of preying on relatively large fish but also supplements its diet with frogs, tadpoles and occasionally shrimp. A large Macleay's Water Snake was seen seizing and swallowing an Oxeye Herring that was 16 cm long. Its main predators are crocodiles and birds, which regularly include Macleay's Water Snakes in their diet. There is also a surprising record of a Northern Long-necked Turtle swallowing a mature Macleay's Water Snake.

the FACTS!

THE GENUS NAME of the Bockadam, *Cerberus,* was coined by the famous French naturalist Georges Cuvier and refers to Cerberus, the three-headed dog of Greek mythology and guardian of the gate to hell.

ALL WATER SNAKES in the family Homalopsidae are rear-fanged and venomous, but are not considered dangerous to humans.

Front-fanged land snakes
— venomous & abundant

MICHAEL CERMAK

Above: Front-fanged land snakes have hollow, syringe-like fangs for the delivery of venom. These have evolved relatively recently.

Order: Squamata **Suborder:** Serpentes
Family: Elapidae **Subfamily:** Elapinae

Australia is renowned for its deadly and dangerous snakes, and rightly so because front-fanged land snakes in the subfamily Elapinae dominate the Australian landscape. Australia has more representatives in this subfamily than in all the other terrestrial snake families combined. No other country on Earth has such an abundance of venomous snakes!

the FACTS!

THE FANGS of the Coastal Taipan (*Oxyuranus scutellatus,* below) are so large, they sometimes wear holes through the snake's bottom jaw.

KEN STEPNELL

IN 1950, publicity surrounding the death of 20-year-old amateur herpetologist Kevin Budden in Cairns, Queensland, from the bite of a Coastal Taipan he had caught 27 hours earlier, became a catalyst for research on its venom at Melbourne's Commonwealth Serum Laboratories. Kevin's snake was the first to be collected alive since 1923 and on his journey to hospital he insisted that it be looked after and forwarded to researchers.

ANTIVENOM is made by injecting small amounts of a snake's venom into a horse over a long time. Eventually, the horse becomes immune to the venom and the horse's "immunised" blood is then used to create an antivenom serum that can be injected into humans.

IN 2006, researchers at the Liverpool School of Tropical Medicine in the UK, found a way to create a synthetic DNA-based antivenom for any species.

ALL VENOMOUS BUT NOT ALL DANGEROUS

Within the subfamily are all of Australia's deadly land snakes, some of which have a venomous potential that is frightening to contemplate. About 25 front-fanged elapid land snakes have the ability to kill humans with their bite, and some of these are common and widespread. Most, however, are not considered deadly or particularly dangerous, although they are all venomous and their bites can produce mild to severe discomfort. Some do not bite at all, even when provoked, while others have tiny fangs that are unlikely to pierce human skin.

VENOM DELIVERY & ANTIVENOM

Venom itself probably evolved long before the syringe-like fangs of venomous snakes came into existence. Front fangs probably evolved from the grooved rear teeth of Colubrid snakes such as the Brown Tree Snake (*Boiga irregularis*). DNA research conducted by Dr Bryan Fry at the University of Melbourne's Venom Research Unit indicates that venom evolved in snakes about 80–60 million years ago and that the toxins originated from harmless proteins produced by other body parts such as the brain, eyes and testes.

Front-fanged land snakes store their venom in glands situated towards the back of the head. The glands are connected to two large, hollow fangs at the front of the upper jaw and attached muscles help empty the venom glands quickly and efficiently, injecting the venom in the same way a hypodermic syringe works. Venom has two main functions: to immobilise prey by attacking its nervous system; and to initiate the snake's digestive process by beginning to breakdown tissue, which is obviously very helpful for an animal that swallows its prey whole. Some highly venomous snakes prove lethal to animals much larger than their usual prey, including humans, so it must be considered that their venomous bite also has a defensive function.

Despite an abundance of dangerous snakes, Australia has a relatively low annual snakebite death rate, which is largely due to the availability of effective antivenom. Australian hospitals are equipped with venom detection kits and by swabbing the bite site, doctors are able to identify the snake species and administer appropriate antivenom.

Left: A Death Adder is milked of its venom to help make antivenom.

STEVE PARISH

MICHAEL CERMAK

Above: The Eastern Brown Snake (*Pseudonaja textilis*) is responsible for more snake bite deaths than any other Australian snake.

WHO'S AFRAID
OF WHOM?

Australia is home to the seven most venomous land snakes on Earth, but despite their ability to inject fatal venom, even the most lethal snakes rarely choose to confront a human. Most of them will quickly retreat when given the chance, but if injured or provoked may readily bite. Some species, however, are common in and adjacent to areas of high human population, which leads to inevitable, though infrequent, life-threatening bites. Fortunately, since antivenom has become available, fatalities rarely occur.

Above: Pale-headed Snake (*Hoplocephalus bitorquatus*)

Above: The Western Brown Snake (*Pseudonaja mengdeni*) inhabits much of mainland Australia.

ALL CORNERS OF THE CONTINENT

Australia is home to some 90 species of front-fanged land snakes, which are widely distributed around the continent and vary greatly in size and appearance.

Some are fully grown at 25 cm, while others grow more than 3 m long. Only two, Stephen's Banded Snake (*Hoplocephalus stephensi*) and the Pale-headed Snake (*Hoplocephalus bitorquatus*) are considered mainly arboreal, although even terrestrial species, such as the Tiger Snake (*Notechis scutatus*) and the Rough-scaled Snake (*Tropidechis carinatus*), may climb into low shrubs to bask or seek food. None could be described as semi-aquatic, but some live on the edge of waterways, lakes and swamps. Front-fanged land snakes may be nocturnal or diurnal, or they may vary their behaviour depending on the prevailing temperature or the region they inhabit.

Small front-fanged land snakes often exclusively eat lizards, especially skinks, while others prefer frogs. Some, like the small shovel-nosed snakes in the genus *Brachyurophis,* eat reptile eggs. Most larger front-fanged land snakes include small mammals and birds in their diet. The bandy bandys in the genus *Vermicella* are food specialists, eating only blind snakes (*Ramphotyphlops* spp.).

the
FACTS!

A NEW SPECIES of taipan has been discovered and named. *Oxyuranus temporalis*, the Central Ranges Taipan, was collected in the remote Walter James Range of Western Australia and to date is known from a single specimen. Scientists are keen to find more snakes for venom research.

WHY A NOCTURNAL REPTILE like the Eastern Bandy Bandy (*Vermicella annulata,* below) has a highly visible pattern of starkly contrasting, black and white rings, is not fully understood. It is thought that when an Eastern Bandy Bandy moves in low light conditions, its banded pattern creates an optical illusion, making it hard for a predator to determine the direction the snake is travelling in.

Top, left to right: King Brown Snake; Coastal Taipan.

the FACTS!

THERE IS NO REAL ANSWER to the frequently asked question "What is the world's deadliest snake?" The deadliest might be the species that kills the most people annually, but others may say it is the species with the most toxic venom. However, some snakes that have a high venom toxicity may produce a low venom yield.

A DANGEROUS SNAKE may bite, but not inject venom. In fact, a large number of defensive bites to humans from Australian venomous snakes fall into this category.

THE KING BROWN SNAKE holds the record for the highest yield taken during venom milking of an Australian snake.

Below: Eastern Brown Snake

TERROR OF THE CANEFIELDS

The Coastal Taipan (*Oxyuranus scutellatus*) is arguably Australia's most dangerous snake, considering its venom toxicity, large size, 13 mm fangs, high venom yield and willingness to bite rapidly and repeatedly when provoked. In the days before the development of a specific antivenom, the mortality rate from the Coastal Taipan's bite was almost total.

At its maximum length of more than 3.5 m, the Coastal Taipan is second in size among Australia's venomous snakes only to the more robust King Brown Snake (*Pseudechis australis*), which occasionally exceeds this length. Although the venom toxicity of the Eastern Brown Snake (*Pseudonaja textilis*), a common and widespread snake of eastern Australia, is more than twice that of the Coastal Taipan, the Coastal Taipan injects up to thirty times as much venom in delivering a bite. So this means that the Coastal Taipan's bite is about ten times more lethal than that of the Eastern Brown Snake. Of course, these comparisons are purely academic, because whether the snake that has bitten you is capable of killing 20 people with a single bite, or indeed just one, you still need to get to the hospital fast!

DROP FOR DROP

According to a procedure called the LD50 test, which draws its conclusions from tests on mice, the much celebrated Western Taipan (*Oxyuranus microlepidotus*, below) possesses the most toxic venom of all the world's snakes. However, it is a shy snake that inhabits only an isolated and sparsely populated region of Australia and therefore poses little actual danger to humans. There are no documented deaths from the bite of the Western Taipan. The snake was originally discovered in north-western Victoria in 1879, but was then more or less forgotten until a further specimen turned up in south-western Queensland almost 100 years later.

Below: The Western Taipan is sometimes also known as the Fierce Snake or Inland Taipan.

Above: Blacksoil Death Adder (*Acanthophis hawkei*)

WATCH YOUR STEP

Vipers are advanced snakes that possess the most sophisticated venom delivery mechanism of all reptiles, with very long, tubular fangs that are hinged and fold back when not in use. They range through most of the world but are absent in Australasia; however, Australia's death adders in the genus *Acanthophis*, although actually elapids, are surprisingly viper-like in their appearance and habits. The similarities between vipers and adders provide a further example of convergent evolution among snakes.

Five death adder species occur across the continent and are totally unlike most other Australian snakes in appearance. Like vipers, they are sedentary (rarely moving about), and have robust bodies and broad, distinct heads. Uniquely among elapid snakes, their long fangs are also somewhat mobile. Death adders are ambush predators that lie motionless and partly concealed among leaf litter and attract their prey by wriggling their grub-like tail tip in the manner of a lure. Over a short distance, a death adder can strike with lightning speed. Unlike most venomous snakes, which usually move out of the way of an approaching human, death adders maintain their camouflaged position and often bite if they are trodden on. When provoked, death adders accentuate their body shape by flattening it into a series of stiff curves. With their long fangs and potent venom they have been responsible for many fatal snakebites.

Above: Northern Death Adders (*Acanthophis praelongus*) are masters of ambush.

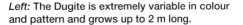

Left: The Dugite is extremely variable in colour and pattern and grows up to 2 m long.

the FACTS!

SNAKEBITE DEATHS average only one or two annually in Australia. To put this in perspective, hundreds of people die each year from the bite of the Papuan Taipan (*Oxyuranus scutellatus canni*) in nearby Papua New Guinea and the beautiful, but very deadly Russell's Viper (*Vipera russelli*), accounts for thousands of deaths in Asia each year.

THE AUSTRALIAN CORAL Snake (*Brachyurophis australis*) is an elapid in the shovel-nosed snake family. It lives in woodland and shrubland and gets it name from its delicate and colourful pattern.

THE BIGGEST KILLER

The Eastern Brown Snake is responsible for the majority of snakebite deaths in Australia. It is common in agricultural areas, where mice provide a ready food supply. It also occurs in the outlying suburbs of eastern Australia's largest cities. The Eastern Brown Snake is a large, athletic snake, with a very high venom toxicity, a mean temperament and a determination to bite when provoked.

A further six kinds of brown snake (*Pseudonaja* spp.) occur throughout Australia. All but one, the Ringed Brown Snake (*Pseudonaja modesta*), are dangerously venomous. The Western Brown Snake (*Pseudonaja mengdeni*) is a highly variable and widely distributed snake in arid and tropical Australia. The Dugite (*Pseudonaja affinis*) is common around Perth, Western Australia.

LEFT & FAR LEFT: STEVE PARISH

Above, left to right and right: Various colour forms of the Tiger Snake.

the FACTS!

MOST front-fanged land snakes lay eggs, but some, mostly in cooler southern localities, bear live young. Tiger Snakes are live-bearers and prolific breeders. Large females have given birth to more than 100 young!

BLACK TIGER SNAKES occur in colder parts of their range. A black (melanotic) colouration enables a reptile to maximise absorption of the sun's rays during overcast weather.

THE RED-BELLIED BLACK Snake was the first Australian terrestrial snake recorded to science. It was described by George Shaw of the British Museum in 1794 from a snake most likely collected near Sydney, New South Wales.

CAPTIVE SPECIMENS of Red-bellied Black Snakes have regurgitated live frogs, leading some researchers to speculate that not all of their prey is affected by the snake's venom. However, it is also possible that on these occasions the prey did not receive any venom.

STEVE PARISH

HISTORIC KILLERS

The Tiger Snake (*Notechis scutatus*) receives its common name from its distinctive bands; however these are not always present. Some races, particularly those in South Australia and the Bass Strait islands, are totally black and have little or no indication of pattern. In the past, such variation has led to misidentification and subsequent complications during snakebite treatment. Australian hospitals are now equipped with venom detection kits that are able to positively identify the snake responsible for a bite from a swab of the bite site. The isolated Tiger Snake populations across southern Australia are now considered to be a single, variable species. All are dangerously venomous and historically they have been responsible for many snakebite deaths. When the early settlers began clearing their selections in south-eastern Australia, it is likely that the Tiger Snake was the dangerous snake they encountered most often. In the days before the availability of antivenom, many Tiger Snake bites proved fatal.

Tiger Snakes inhabit temperate regions with regular rainfall and can be abundant in a suitable environment. This habitat preference brings them into contact with about 80% of Australians, who prefer a similar habitat. In dry areas and high-altitude forest in the north of their range, they are confined to the fringes of rivers and creeks. Tiger Snakes are generally most common near creeks or swamps, where the frogs on which they feed are in abundance. They forage by day or on warm nights and, although terrestrial, may climb shrubs to search for prey. Larger Tiger Snakes will eat birds (those on islands often eat seabirds), mammals and other small snakes as well as amphibians.

Below: A Chappell Island Tiger Snake devours a muttonbird chick.

MICHAEL CERMAK

Conservation Watch

The Broad-headed Snake is listed as Vulnerable and has a small distribution centred around Sydney, Australia's largest city. It is threatened by urban expansion and has been displaced from much of its former range.

AN **UNDESERVED** REPUTATION

With its eye-catching colouration, the Red-bellied Black Snake (*Pseudechis porphyriacus,* left) is a familiar snake to people in eastern Australia. Australian folklore often painted the Red-bellied Black Snake as an aggressive killer; but in reality, although it is dangerously venomous, only one fatality is on record. Its venom is less toxic than that of other large front-fanged land snakes, and it is quick to retreat and generally reluctant to bite.

Red-bellied Black Snakes feed mainly on frogs, but also eat mammals, lizards and occasionally eels. Northern populations appeared to decline — probably as a result of these snakes attempting to eat the poisonous Cane Toad — but its numbers are now recovering, as the snakes adjust to an ecosystem where the introduced Cane Toad is a permanent resident.

THREATENED BY MAN

The beautifully patterned Broad-headed Snake (*Hoplocephalus bungaroides*) is considered Vulnerable because of its restricted distribution in a densely populated region of New South Wales, centred around Sydney. Unfortunately for the Broad-headed Snake, its preferred habitat of sandstone ridges also makes for prime real estate and the houses of an expanding suburbia are rapidly taking over. Any snakes surviving in adjacent bushland are soon cleaned up by domestic cats that often accompany the houses. In addition, the lichen-encrusted sandstone rocks under which the snakes shelter are much sought after as "bush rock" for gardens, and in some areas have been extensively removed. The Broad-headed Snake's main chance of survival lies in the large areas of habitat remaining somewhat intact in the expansive national parks of the Sydney region.

Right: Broad-headed Snakes shelter in crevices of Sydney sandstone.

WHIP SNAKES

Australia has eight whip snake species in the genus *Demansia* and all are swift, slender, mildly venomous snakes with characteristic long tapering tails that resemble the thin end of a whip. One of the most variable species is the Yellow-faced Whip Snake (*Demansia psammophis*), which includes a number of widely distributed subspecies. Yellow-faced Whip Snakes are one of the few Australian snake species to use communal nesting sites and as many as 600 eggs have been found in a single nest.

Left: The Yellow-faced Whip Snake has three recognised subspecies, including *Demansia psammophis psammophis*.

Above: Elegant Sea Snakes (*Hydrophis elegans*) feed on eels and are dangerously venomous.

Marine snakes
— sea snakes & sea kraits

Order: Squamata **Suborder:** Serpentes
Family: Elapidae **Subfamilies:** Hydrophiinae & Laticaudinae

*Most marine snakes live in the warm tropical waters of the Indo-Pacific region, but occasional individuals and one open-ocean (pelagic) species, the Yellow-bellied Sea Snake (*Pelamis platurus*), swim much further afield. About 30 species of marine snakes have been recorded in Australian waters.*

IN GENERAL, MARINE SNAKES inhabit shallow waters close to the coast and islands. Some species, such as the Spotted Sea Snake (*Hydrophis ornatus*) frequent coral reefs in open waters; others like the Black-ringed Mangrove Snake (*Hydrelaps darwiniensis*) haunt the intertidal zone in shallow, mangrove-fringed estuaries.

the FACTS!

MOST MARINE SNAKES are dangerously venomous, but there are no recorded fatalities in Australia from their bite. However, deaths do occur regularly in other countries.

PEOPLE AND MARINE SNAKES do not often cross paths, so bites are quite rare. People are most likely to be bitten if they have to remove snakes from fishing nets or, in the case of commercial fishing, when they are sorting their catch.

LUCKILY FOR FISHERS, more often than not marine snakes do not inject venom when they bite defensively.

THE COMMONWEALTH SERUM LABORATORY has developed an antivenom that is largely effective in neutralising the venom of a wide variety of marine snakes.

STEVE PARISH

Above: Sea snakes are excellent swimmers but struggle to move on land.

EXCELLENT SWIMMERS

With their elongate bodies, snakes in general are good swimmers, but the marine snakes benefit from paddle-shaped tails that are superbly adapted to the aquatic environment. Some have a laterally compressed body and a ventral keel, which further enhances their stability and manoeuvrability in the water. Marine snakes have valvular nostrils that remain firmly closed while the snake is diving. Incredibly, they can remain underwater for up to two hours before returning to the surface to breathe, because they are able to take up some of their oxygen requirement from the water through their skin.

SEA CHANGE

It is now widely accepted that marine snakes evolved from terrestrial elapid snakes and that their move to the marine environment was a relatively recent one. Like their land-based relatives, they are front-fanged and most are dangerously venomous.

SEA SNAKES

Sea snakes in the subfamily Hydrophiinae are the world's only fully marine reptiles. The young are born alive in the water, so sea snakes have no reason to venture onto the land. When they are washed ashore during storms they have great difficulty progressing on dry land and usually perish.

RON & VALERIE TAYLOR

Conservation Watch

Thousands of marine snakes are caught as by-catch in trawler nets each year, but the impact of this industry on sea snake populations remains unstudied.

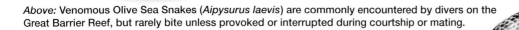

Above: Venomous Olive Sea Snakes (*Aipysurus laevis*) are commonly encountered by divers on the Great Barrier Reef, but rarely bite unless provoked or interrupted during courtship or mating.

FISH EATERS

Most marine snakes eat fish. Some, like the Small-headed Sea Snake (*Hydrophis mcdowelli*), have a very small head, narrow anterior (front) body and disproportionately large posterior (rear) body, a design that enables them to seek out eels in tight crevices among coral.

Typically, marine snakes forage on the bottom of the sea in much the same manner as a snake might do on dry land. The exception is the pelagic Yellow-bellied Sea Snake, which drifts on warm currents at the surface, usually among debris and often far from land. It feeds on small fish that seek shelter beneath the floating debris or sometimes beneath the floating snake. The Yellow-bellied Sea Snake is the most widespread snake species on Earth, ranging throughout the Pacific and Indian Oceans, from the west coast of the Americas to the east coast of Africa. They are occasionally washed ashore in temperate Australia as far south as Victoria and Tasmania. As an inhabitant of the open sea, the Yellow-bellied Sea Snake has no access to rocks or coral to assist it while shedding its skin; instead, it ties itself in knots and rubs the skin off on its own coils while knotting and unknotting its body.

the FACTS!

DUBOIS' Sea Snake (*Aipysurus duboisii*, above) possesses one of the most toxic sea snake venoms, but no deaths have occurred from its bite.

MARINE SNAKES SHED their skin more regularly than land snakes. It is very important for them to rid the skin of algae and barnacles to maintain their swimming efficiency.

A BUILD-UP OF SALT is excreted from a sea snake's body from a gland located beneath the tongue.

AUSTRALIA'S two recorded sea krait species are the Yellow-lipped Sea Krait (*Laticauda colubrina*) and the Brown-lipped Sea Krait (*Laticauda laticaudata,* below).

A FISH EGG SPECIALIST

Above: Turtle-headed Sea Snakes are harmless.

The Turtle-headed Sea Snake (*Emydocephalus annulatus*) feeds only on fish eggs, which it scrapes from the surface of rocks and coral with the highly modified, plate-like scales of its upper lips. Its short, blunt head is almost turtle-like in appearance, hence its common name. The Turtle-headed Sea Snake is harmless. Its venom apparatus has degenerated because of its specialised feeding habits.

SEA KRAITS

The sea kraits in the subfamily Laticaudinae are best described as amphibious. They are egg layers that must come ashore to lay their eggs and they also regularly leave the water to bask or rest. Large numbers of sea kraits are sometimes present on small islands, or around exposed, rusting shipwrecks.

Two species of sea krait are occasionally found in Australian waters, but there are no resident populations and they do not lay their eggs on the Australian mainland. Because they negotiate dry land as well as water, their basic body form is rather cylindrical, similar to that of a terrestrial elapid snake, but they still have a laterally flattened, paddle-like tail.

Reptiles & people
— loved or loathed?

Australians have varying attitudes to reptiles, usually ranging from intolerance to indifference. However, a growing number now look on them more favourably than they did a generation ago.

HERPETOLOGISTS (PEOPLE WHO STUDY REPTILES) choose to make them their life's work and herpetoculturists (people who keep reptiles as pets) love their reptiles as other people love the family dog. Even those people who are frightened of reptiles, usually cannot help but admit to being fascinated by them. However, reptiles are still unnecessarily persecuted by some people, invariably because of ignorance.

Snakes and crocodiles are the main focus of human hostility but many other reptiles, such as harmless legless lizards and other lizards, suffer because of their affiliation with these more formidable reptiles. Most people fear or dislike reptiles only because they do not understand them. It is, perhaps, hard to relate to animals such as snakes that have no legs yet can move across the ground with such ease and fluidity — and, of course, there is the fact that snakes have a venomous bite and are prepared to use it to defend themselves. People are right to be wary of dangerous reptiles, but we must remember that reptiles too are attempting to share their habitats with potentially deadly adversaries — us!

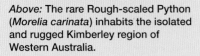

Above: The rare Rough-scaled Python (*Morelia carinata*) inhabits the isolated and rugged Kimberley region of Western Australia.

IAN MORRIS

the FACTS!

WONAMBI, one of the many Aboriginal names for the mythical Rainbow Serpent, is also the name given to an extinct 5 m, python-like snake, *Wonambi naracoortensis*, that inhabited Australia until some 50,000 years ago. It has been suggested that Wonambi is the source of the Rainbow Serpent legend.

A SNAKE'S ABILITY to periodically renew itself by shedding off its entire skin, leaving behind scars and blemishes and emerging, gleaming and new, led primitive people to associate them with healing and immortality. The medical symbol, two snakes entwined around a staff, has its origins in such beliefs.

LEFT: STEVE PARISH

Above, left and right: Lizards are becoming increasingly popular as children's pets in many parts of the world.

ONCE WERE WORSHIPPED

Snakes were not always so reviled, in very early times people on all inhabited continents of the Earth worshipped the divine serpent. Snake worship, in one form or another, is perhaps the most widespread mythology known to humankind. In Australia, the Rainbow Serpent is the most significant and powerful being of Aboriginal mythology. Aborigines believe that during the Dreamtime (the time of the Earth's creation) the Rainbow Serpent undertook a great "walkabout" (journey) across the then flat, featureless surface of the Earth. As it journeyed, it pushed up the mountains and gouged out channels that would later become the rivers.

Left: Snakes are frequently represented in Aboriginal rock art.

STEVE PARISH

Above: Aboriginal children fearlessly encounter an Estuarine Crocodile (*Crocodylus porosus*) on a Northern Territory Beach.

Above: Aquariums are great places to introduce children to marine reptiles.

AN IMPORTANT FOOD SOURCE FOR ABORIGINES

Australian Aborigines have long recognised the importance of reptiles; lizards, snakes, turtles and crocodiles are a significant part of their diet. Evidence of their importance is signified by the many depictions of these animals in rock art galleries at sites throughout northern Australia.

In central Australia, Aboriginal women use digging sticks to extricate monitor lizards from their burrows, while across northern Australia Indigenous hunters feel about beneath submerged logs in the billabongs for aquatic file snakes and freshwater turtles. However, it is not only Aboriginal Australians who eat reptiles. In the Northern Territory, commercial crocodile farms produce crocodile meat as well as skins. Darwin's Fort Hill Wharf is a popular venue for tourists seeking an open air, tropical dining experience and crocodile burgers are on the menu.

"SNAKE MEN"

Today, we learn all about snakes by switching on the Discovery Channel, but 100 years ago the public learned all about snakes from "snake men" (and occasionally "snake women") — professional showpeople, who toured the countryside showing snakes at fairs and public events.

During the show, the snake man would perform various acts of bravado with dangerous snakes and, as a profitable sideline, peddle his patented snakebite antidote to the public. The ingredients of each snake man's "cure" were a closely guarded secret. When bitten during the show, as they regularly were, the remedy was applied and the result was often a seemingly "miraculous" recovery. It is likely that many snake men genuinely believed that their "cure" had saved their life, despite others who were bitten having died. When a snake bites defensively, it does not inject venom on about 90% of

Above: Nowadays, people can enjoy the thrill of a modern snake exhibition (run by the Cann family) at La Perouse in Botany Bay National Park.

occasions, so the odds were in the snake man's favour nine times out of ten. Also, unbeknown to the snake men, many of them carried antibodies to the venom in their bloodstream as the result of receiving many small doses of venom over a period of time, so some had probably developed a degree of immunity, at least to some species of snakes.

the FACTS!

"PROFESSOR" FRED FOX, Australia's most famous snake man of the 1900s, had so much faith in his snakebite antidote, that he travelled to India to demonstrate its effectiveness. During one demonstration, he allowed himself to be bitten on the wrist by a highly venomous krait in the genus *Bungarus*. He applied his "cure", but died from the effects of the bite later that evening.

FIRST AID FOR SNAKEBITE:
- Stay calm.
- Do not cut the bitten area.
- Do not wash, clean or wipe the bitten area.
- If the bite is on a limb (they usually are), firmly apply a broad, elasticised bandage to the entire limb (or substitute torn strips of clothing if a bandage is not available).
- Bind the limb firmly, as you would for a sprain, but not so tight as to cut off the circulation.
- Immobilise the limb in a sling or splint.
- If possible, get transport, rather than walk. Never run.
- Go to the nearest hospital without delay.

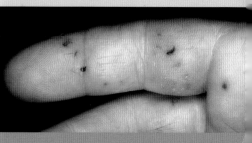

RIGHT & FAR RIGHT: IAN MORRIS

REPTILE RESEARCH

Modern "snake men" are called herpetologists, and through their determined efforts, we are beginning to unlock some of the many mysteries of reptiles. In Australia, reptile species that are new to science are regularly discovered. The Pygmy Blue-tongue had not been sighted for 33 years until, in 1992, a herpetologist who was examining a bulge in the stomach of a road-killed Eastern Brown Snake made an astonishing discovery — the bulge was a recently swallowed Pygmy Blue-tongue. Only another herpetologist can imagine the rush of excitement he must have experienced. In 1993 the Nangur Spiny Skink, a skink so different that it occupies a genus of its own, was discovered in vine forest a few hours drive from Brisbane, Queensland's largest city. In 1994, the Mary River Turtle, also so different to other turtles that it was placed in a genus of its own, was described from the Mary River of south-eastern Queensland. With a shell length of over 40 cm, it is one of Australia's largest freshwater turtles. More new discoveries no doubt await herpetologists and reptile enthusiasts who are eager to go out into the field and work with these fascinating animals.

STEVE PARISH

Top and above: Many wildlife parks provide an opportunity for children to handle reptiles safely.

PUSHED TO THE BRINK

No Australian reptile is known to have become extinct since 1788, but that does not mean that European settlement of Australia hasn't adversely affected reptiles. Today, there are probably only about 100 Western Swamp Turtles (the world's most endangered turtle) left in the wild. In 1869, Gerard Krefft of the Australian Museum stated that the beautiful Broad-headed Snake was common along the rocky foreshore from the entrance of Port Jackson to Botany Bay; needless to say, there are no Broad-headed Snakes there today, just bitumen roads and high-rise buildings. Sydney's continuing urban expansion further threatens the endangered Broad-headed Snake's survival. The Mary River in south-eastern Queensland has been earmarked for the huge Traveston Crossing dam, but is the sole habitat of the unique and endangered Mary River Turtle, populations of which will almost certainly decline dramatically, or disappear entirely, if the dam goes ahead. As long as humans continue to exploit, degrade and destroy Australia's natural habitats, the future for reptiles, and for all native fauna, is at risk.

IAN MORRIS

STEVE PARISH

Left: An Aboriginal Park Ranger with a marine turtle.

Right: Field research is crucial to conservation efforts for endangered reptile species.

Glossary

AESTIVATE A period of inactivity during hot weather or summer.

AMPHIBIAN A four-limbed, cold-blooded animal that lives both on land and in water over its life cycle.

ANTIVENOM A serum used to treat people who have been bitten by a venomous snake.

AQUATIC Living in water.

ARBOREAL Living in trees.

ARID Dry, parched with heat.

CAMOUFLAGE Protective colouration that blends in with the background.

CARNIVORE An animal that eats other animals, e.g. a monitor lizard.

CLASSIFICATION The process of naming and identifying things.

CLOACA Single opening at the end of the digestive tract for both exoretory and reproductive process.

CLUTCH The number of eggs a female reptile lays.

COILED Wound into loops.

COLONISE To become established in a new habitat.

CONSTRICT To coil tightly around prey until it is unable to breathe.

CONVERGENT EVOLUTION Unrelated animals that have evolved similar features or behaviour to suit similar environmental conditions.

DIURNAL Being active during the day.

EMBRYO An animal in a developmental stage between conception and birth.

ENDEMIC Having evolved in a particular country or region and existing nowhere else.

EXTINCT When an animal, plant, or other living organism ceases to exist.

FANG A hollow or grooved tooth used to inject venom.

FERAL Having reverted to a wild state.

GENETICS The way certain physical features are transmitted from parent to offspring by means of genes.

GENUS The classification of a group of organisms that share many characteristics; a genus may contain one or more species.

GESTATION Time between conception and birth.

HABITAT The place where a particular animal or plant lives or grows.

HERBIVORE An animal that eats plants.

HERPETOLOGIST A scientist who studies reptiles.

HIBERNATION Period of prolonged inactivity and lowered metabolism brought about by cold weather.

IMMUNE Protected from poison or disease by having been previously exposed to it.

INCUBATE To keep eggs warm so they develop and hatch.

INSECTIVORE An animal that eats mainly insects.

INVERTEBRATE An animal without a backbone.

KEELED SCALE One or more raised ridges running lengthwise along the middle of each scale.

LABIAL Of the lips, usually referring to scales bordering the lips.

LINNEAN SYSTEM Plant and animal classification developed by Carl von Linnaeus in the 18th century.

METABOLISM Chemical processes that sustain life.

NATIVE An animal or plant species belonging to the land, as distinguished from foreign species.

NOCTURNAL Active at night.

OMNIVORE An animal that eats plants and animals.

PARALYSIS Loss of control over the muscles.

PREDATOR An animal that hunts and eats other animals.

PREHENSILE Able to grip.

RODENTS Group of gnawing animals, including mice and rats.

SCAVENGER Animals that eat dead animals.

SLOUGH To shed the skin.

SPECIES A group of organisms that can breed to produce fertile offspring with similar characteristics.

SPURS The tiny remains of legs that are found on pythons.

TAXONOMY The science of classifying (describing and naming) plants and animals.

TERRESTRIAL Living on land.

TERRITORIAL Related to the defence of a territory.

TERRITORY Area occupied and defended by an individual or group.

TORPOR State of inactivity, usually brought about by cold. An animal's metabolic rate slows down and it uses less food reserves.

TOXIC Poisonous.

VENOM A toxic substance made by animals and then injected into prey using fangs, spines or stingers.

VERTEBRATES Animals with backbones. Includes fish, amphibians, reptiles, birds, mammals.

WOODLAND Area sparsely covered with trees.

Index

A

Acanthophis
  antarcticus 49, 55
  praelongus 7, 71
  pyrrhus 49
Acrochordus
  arafurae 6, 62
  granulatus 62
Aipysurus
  duboisii 6, 75
  laevis 75
Amphibolurus
  burnsi 39, 42
  gilberti 39
  longirostris 40
  muricatus 15, 38
  temporalis 40
Antaresia
  perthensis 60
  stimsoni 9
Antilopine Wallaroo 17
Aprasia inaurita 36
Aspidites
  melanocephalus 59
  ramsayi 59
Austrelaps ramsayi 6

B

Bellatorias
  major 49
  obiri 49
Blue-tongue
  Centralian 49
  Eastern 9, 49
  Pygmy 50
Bockadam 66, 67
Boiga irregularis 11, 55, 64, 68
Brachyurophis australis 71
Burton's Snake-lizard 36, 37

C

Caretta caretta 13, 20
Carettochelys insculpta 15, 24, 29
Carlia
  gracilis 51
  jarnoldae 51
  pectoralis 12
  rufilatus 30
Carphodactylus laevis 35
Cerberus australis 67
Chelodina
  longicollis 6, 25
  rugosa 25
  steindachneri 25
Chelonia mydas 6, 20
Chelosania brunnea 43
Chlamydosaurus kingii 10, 12, 15, 42, 43
Coeranoscincus frontalis 48, 51
Corallus caninus 59
Crocodile 16–19
  Freshwater 8, 14, 16, 18, 19, 60
  Estuarine 5, 7, 9, 14, 15, 16, 17, 18, 19, 21, 77
Crocodylus
  johnstoni 8, 14, 16, 60
  porosus 5, 7, 14, 16, 77
Cryptoblepharus pulcher 6, 9, 49, 52
Cryptophis
  incredibilis 71
  nigrescens 11
Ctenophorus
  caudicinctus 6, 41

cristatus 43
  decresii 12
  maculosus 6
  nuchalis 10, 43
  pictus 38
  vadnappa 12, 38
Ctenotus strauchii 53
Cyclodomorphus gerrardii 52
Cyrtodactylus tuberculatus 33

D

Death Adder
  Common 49, 55
  Desert 49
  Northern 7, 68, 71
Delma
  Excitable 37
  Single-striped 36, 37
Delma
  labialis 36, 37
  impar 37
Demansia
  psammophis 11, 73
    psammophis 73
Dendrelaphis
  calligastra 65
  punctulata 11, 65
Dermochelys coriacea 20
Diplodactylus
  conspicillatus 34
  galeatus 34
Diporiphora
  australis 43
  bennettii 40
  linga 43
  magna 38
  reginae 43
  winneckei 39
Dragon
  Bennett's Two-lined 40
  Boyd's Forest 40, 43
  Burns' 39, 42
  Canegrass Two-lined 39
  Central Bearded 10, 15
  Central Netted 10, 43
  Chameleon 43
  Crested 43
  Dwarf Bearded 41
  Eastern Bearded 41
  Eastern Water 40
  Eyrean Earless 39
  Gilbert's 39
  Gippsland Water 4, 40
  Grassland Earless 39, 42
  Komodo 30, 44, 47
  Lake Eyre 6
  Long-nosed Water 40
  Mitchell's Bearded 41
  Mountain 43, 48
  Northern Water 40
  Painted 38
  Pebble Earless 41, 42
  Pink Two-line 43
  Plain-backed Two-lined 43
  Red-barred 12, 38
  Ring-tailed 41
  Southern Forest 10, 43
  Tawny 12
  Water 38
  Yellow-sided Two-lined 38
Dtella
  Eastern 30
  Northern 31, 32, 35
  Variegated 35
Dugite 71

E

Eastern Bandy Bandy 69
Egernia
  cunninghami 7, 11, 48
  depressa 48
  frerei 48
  saxatilis 11
  stokesii 11, 53
Elseya
  irwini 27
Elusor macrurus 26, 28
Emerald Tree Boa 59
Emydocephalus annulatus 75
Emydura
  macquarii
    emmotti 28
    signata 9
  subglobosa 29
  victoriae 27
Epinephelus coioides 10
Eremiascincus
  fasciolatus 6, 52
  richardsonii 52
Eretmochelys imbricata 6, 20
Eulamprus
  quoyii 49
  tympanum 15

F

Fordonia leucobalia 6, 66
Furina dunmalli 69

G

Gecko
  Arnhem Land Cave 35
  Asian House 13, 32
  Barking see also Thick-tailed Gecko 33
  Centralian Prickly Knob-tailed 34
  Chameleon 35
  Eastern Prickly Knob-tailed 34
  Eungella Banded-tailed 35
  Fat-tailed 34
  Hammer-tailed 34
  Helmeted 34
  Jean's Striped 35
  Jewelled 35
  Marbled Velvet 32, 34
  Mourning 12
  North African Helmeted 32
  Pernatty Knob-tailed 35
  Ring-tailed 33
  Southern Banded-tailed 33
  Southern Leaf-tailed 10, 35
  Southern Spotted Velvet 35
  Thick-tailed 33
  Western Smooth Knob-tailed 35
  White-striped 32
Gehyra
  australis 30, 32, 35
  variegata 35
Gila Monster 10
Gnypetoscincus
  queenslandiae 6
Goanna see also Monitor
  Canopy 47
Goldspotted Rockcod 10

H

Heloderma
  horridum 10

suspectum 10
Hemiaspis signata 54
Hemidactylus frenatus 13, 32
Highland Copperhead 6
Hoplocephalus
  bitorquatus 69
  bungaroides 73
  stephensi 69
Hydrelaps darwiniensis 74
Hydrophis
  mcdowelli 75
  ornatus 74
Hypsilurus
  boydii 40, 43
  spinipes 10, 43

K

Kalisuchus 5
Keelback 64, 65

L

Lampropholis
  delicata 11, 48, 53
  guichenoti 30, 49
Land Mullet 49, 52
Lanthanotus borneensis 54
Laticauda colubrina 11, 75
Latrodectus hasselti 10
Lepidochelys olivacea 20
Lepidodactylus lugubris 12
Lerista labialis 51
Lialis
  burtonis 9, 36, 37
  mackloti 60
  olivaceus
    barroni 7, 61
    olivaceus 61
Liopholis whitii 53
Lizard
  Beaded 10
  Burton's Snake 9
  Frilled 10, 12, 15, 42, 43
  Jacky 15, 38
  Pine Cone See also Shingleback 50
  Sleepy. See also Shingleback 50
  Two-headed See also Shingleback 50
Lycodon aulicus capucinus 64

M

Macropus antilopinus 16
Mangrove Snake
  White-bellied 7, 10, 66
  Richardson's Mangrove 66
Megalania prisca 47
Menetia alanae 30, 49
Moloch horridus 6, 30, 41
Monitor
  African Savannah 45
  Black-palmed Rock 45
  Earless 54
  Emerald 54
  Freckled 7, 46
  Heath 45, 47
  Lace 6, 7, 10, 47
  Mangrove 45
  Mertens' Water 5, 44
  Mitchell's Water 10, 45
  Sand 45, 47
  Spiny-tailed 45
  Spotted Tree 46
  Yellow-spotted 7, 12, 44, 46
Morelia
  carinata 60, 76

kinghorni 54, 58
  oenpelliensis 57, 60
  spilota 61
  spilota
    cheynei 61
    mcdowelli 58, 61
    spilota 61
  viridis 14, 59, 61
Muttaburrasaurus 4
Myron richardsonii 66

N

Nangura spinosa 53
Natator depressus 20
Nephrurus
  amyae 34
  asper 34
  deleani 35
  levis occidentalis 35
Niveoscincus
  ocellatus 15
  palfreymani 48
Notechis scutatus 11, 54, 69, 72

O

Oedura
  marmorata 32
  tryoni 35
Ophioscincus
  cooloolensis 52
  ophioscincus 52
  truncatus 52
Oxyuranus
  microlepidotus 70
  scutellatus 68, 70, 71
    canni 71
  temporalis 69

P

Paradelma orientalis 37
Pelamis platurus 74
Perentie 30, 44, 47
Phyllurus
  caudiannulatus 33
  nepthys 35
Physignathus
  howittii 40
  lesueurii 40
    lesueurii 40
Pogona
  barbata 41
  mitchelli 41
  vitticeps 10, 15
Pseudechis
  australis 10, 59, 70
  porphyriacus 9, 73
Pseudemydura umbrina 25, 29
Pseudobradypus 4
Pseudonaja
  affinis 71
  mengdeni 69, 71
  modesta 71
  nuchalis 10
  textilis 11, 50, 69, 70
Pseudothecadactylus
  lindneri 35
Pygopus
  nigriceps 37
  schraderi 10, 36
Python
  Ball 61
  Black-headed 58, 59
  Bluff Downs Giant 61
  Diamond 61
  Eastern Carpet 58, 61
  Green Tree 14, 59, 61
  Jungle Carpet 61

Oenpelli 57, 60
Olive 7, 61
Pilbara Olive 7, 61
Pygmy 60
Reticulated 58
Rough-scaled 60, 76
Scrub 54, 58
Stimson's 9
Water 58, 60
Python
  regius 61
  reticulatus 58

R

Ramphotyphlops
  australis 56
  braminus 12, 54, 56
  ligatus 56
  longissimus 57
  nigrescens 11, 57
  wiedii 57
Rankinia diemensis 43, 48
Red-backed Spider 10
Red-tailed Worm-lizard 36
Rheodytes leukops 26

S

Saltuarius swaini 10, 35
Sand Swimmer
  Broad-banded 52
  Narrow-banded 6, 52
Scaly-foot
  Brigalow 37
  Eastern Hooded 10, 36
  Southern 37
  Western Hooded 37
Sea Krait
  Brown-lipped 75
  Yellow-lipped 11, 75
Sea Snake
  Olive 75
  Dubois' 6, 75
  Small-headed 75
  Spotted 74
  Turtle-headed 75
  Yellow-bellied 74, 75
Shingleback 49, 50
Skink
  Black Rock 11
  Cooloola Snake 52
  Cunningham's 7, 11, 48
  Delicate 11, 48, 53
  Depressed Spiny 48
  Fence 6, 9, 49, 52
  Garden 30, 49
  Golden Water 49
  Jewel Rainbow 51
  Limbless Snake-tooth 48
  Major 49
  Nangur Spiny 53, 78
  Obiri Rock 49
  Ocellated 15
  Open Litter Rainbow 12
  Orange-bellied Snake 52
  Pedra Branca 48
  Pink-tongued 52
  Red-sided Rainbow 30
  Short-limbed Snake 52
  Slender Rainbow 51
  Southern Water 15
  Spiny-tailed 11, 53
  Strauch's Striped 53
  Top End Dwarf 30, 31, 49
  White's 53
Slider, Southern 51
Snake
  Arafura File 6, 62, 63
  Asian Wolf 64